REVISED AND EXPANDED
GIANT MORE BASIC SKILLS™
K–1 WORKBOOK

Modern Publishing
A Division of Unisystems, Inc.
New York, New York 10022
Series UPC #49105

D1307452

Cover art by Francesca Rizzo
Illustrated by Arthur Friedman
Educational Consultant, Shereen Gertel Rutman, M.S.

Copyright © 2000 by Modern Publishing,
a division of Unisystems, Inc.

™ Revised and Expanded Giant More Basic Skills K–1 Workbook
is a trademark of Modern Publishing, a division of Unisystems, Inc.

Printed in the U.S.A.

TO THE PARENTS

Dear Parents,

As your child's first and most important teacher, you can encourage your child's love of learning by participating in educational activities at home. Working together on the activities in this workbook will help your child build confidence, learn to reason, and develop skills necessary for early childhood education.

The following are some suggestions to help make your time together both enjoyable and rewarding.

- Choose a time when you and your child are relaxed.

- Provide a writing utensil that your child is familiar with.

- Don't attempt to do too many pages at one time or expect that every page be completed. Move on if your child is frustrated or loses interest.

- Discuss each page. Help your child relate the concepts in this book to everyday experiences.

- Encourage your child to use the practice pages provided at the end of the COLORS, SHAPES AND NUMBERS and BASIC MATH SKILLS sections to work independently and reinforce skills.

- Use the Achievement Checklist to keep track of which pages you need to revisit. When the "Mastered" column is full, your child has earned the diploma at the back of the book!

ESSENTIAL SKILLS

The repetitive activities within each chapter have been designed to help children learn the organizational skills necessary for learning and thinking.

CHAPTER 1 Handwriting Skills

Learning to control the small muscles of the hand (**fine motor skill development**) allows the child to make the precise movements necessary for forming letters, while **writing from left to right**, **tracing**, and **forming lines** help to refine **eye/hand coordination**. Making **associations**—recognizing what things "go together"—enables a child to recognize that an uppercase "A" and lowercase "a" go together.

CHAPTER 2 Colors, Shapes, and Numbers

Looking at familiar shapes helps children notice similarities and differences. Activities in which the child reproduces shapes and/or matches shapes to words encourage **sight vocabulary recognition** and the ability to make **associations between words and objects**. Grouping things according to common attributes such as color, shape, etc. (**classification**) encourages development of reasoning ability and **logical connections**. **Recognizing number words**, **writing numerals**, and **forming sets** all prepare a child for basic math.

CHAPTER 3 Basic Math Skills

Becoming familiar with the **order of numbers from 1–10**, **learning to write those numbers**, and **understanding the connection between a set and its corresponding numeral** all prepare a child to understand addition and subtraction. **Observing and continuing patterns** and **measuring** help children develop logical reasoning skills.

CHAPTER 4 Time and Money

In this chapter children learn about the **numbers on the clock** and how to **tell time to the hour and half hour**. Children also explore money concepts using **pennies, nickels, and dimes**.

CHAPTER 5 Reading Readiness

Determining which items in a group "go together" (**making associations**) and learning to group things according to common attributes (**classification**) prepare a child to **notice details**.

PHONICS RIDDLE BOOK

This special section features rhyming riddles about people and their jobs. Initial consonants are clues to the riddles, and groups of pictures reinforce each letter, while other phonics concepts are highlighted for observation.

CHAPTER 6 Phonics Skills I

This chapter focuses on teaching a child to recognize the **initial and final consonant sounds**, learn to **write letters and words** using these sounds, and understand the **association between sounds, symbols, and words**.

CHAPTER 7 Phonics Skills II

Phonics II focuses on training a child to **hear and reproduce the long and short vowel sounds**, as well as the sounds made by combining two letters to make **consonant blends and digraphs**.

TABLE OF CONTENTS

HANDWRITING SKILLS

Trace and color the picture.

Skills: Tracing; Fine motor skill development; Eye/hand coordination

HANDWRITING SKILLS

Trace and color the picture.

Skills: Tracing; Fine motor skill development; Eye/hand coordination

HANDWRITING SKILLS

Start at the dots. Trace the broken lines.

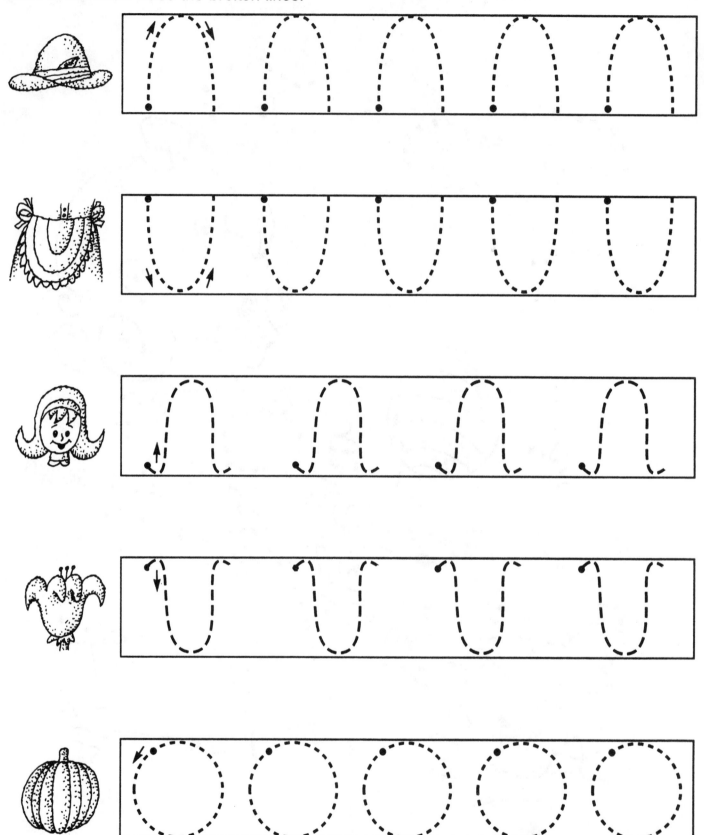

Skills: Fine motor skill development; Eye/hand coordination; Forming open and closed curves

HANDWRITING SKILLS

Start at the dots. Trace the broken lines. Then finish the page.

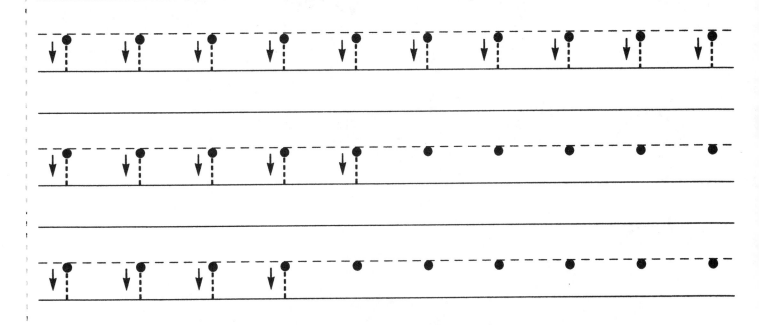

Skills: Fine motor skill development; Eye/hand coordination; Forming vertical lines

HANDWRITING SKILLS

Start at the dots. Trace the broken lines. Then finish the page.

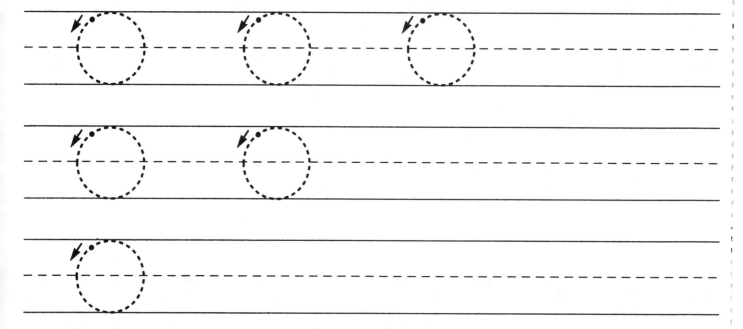

Skills: Fine motor skill development; Eye/hand coordination; Forming closed curves

HANDWRITING SKILLS

Start at the dots. Trace the broken lines. Then finish the page.

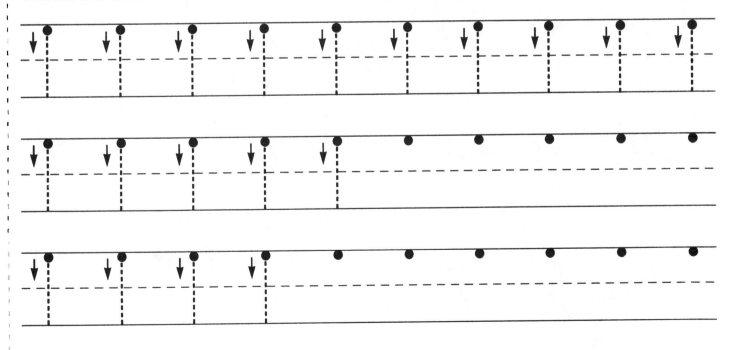

Skills: Fine motor skill development; Eye/hand coordination; Forming vertical lines

HANDWRITING SKILLS

Start at the dots. Trace the broken lines. Then finish the page.

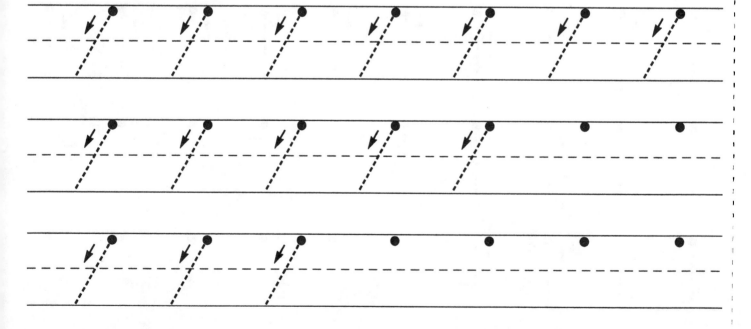

Skills: Fine motor skill development; Eye/hand coordination; Forming diagonal lines

HANDWRITING SKILLS

Start at the dots. Trace the broken lines. Then finish the page.

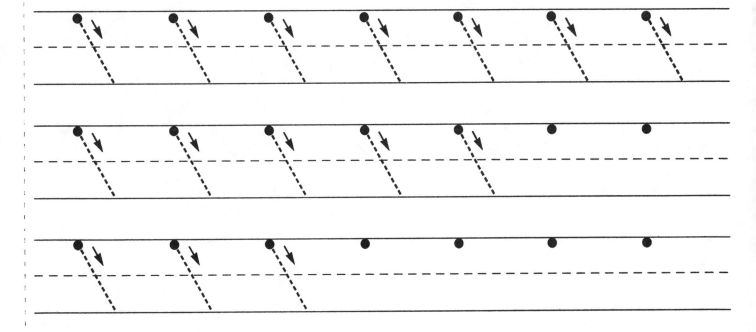

Skills: Fine motor skill development; Eye/hand coordination; Forming diagonal lines

HANDWRITING SKILLS

Start at the dots. Trace the broken lines. Then finish the page.

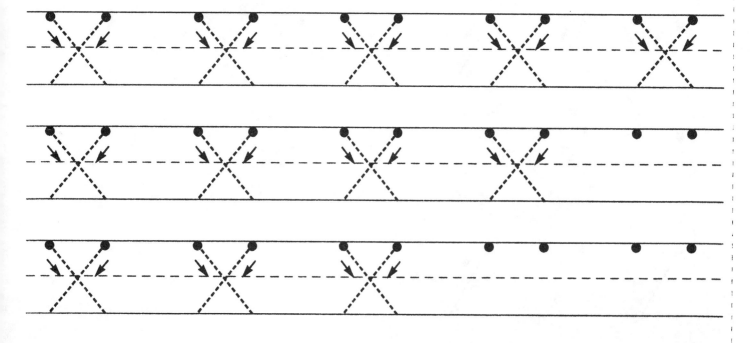

Skills: Fine motor skill development; Eye/hand coordination; Forming diagonal lines

HANDWRITING SKILLS

Start at the dots. Trace the broken lines. Then finish the page.

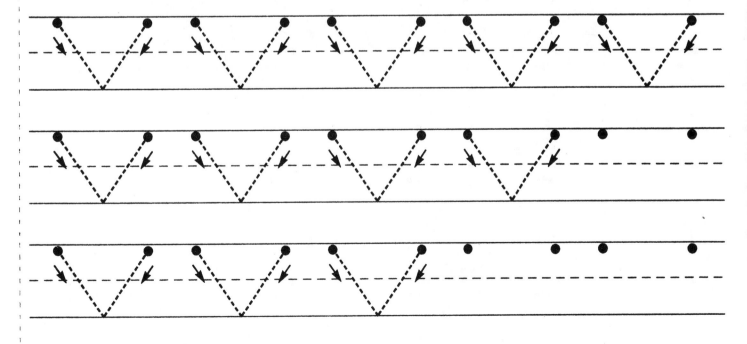

Skills: Fine motor skill development; Eye/hand coordination; Forming diagonal lines

HANDWRITING SKILLS

Start at the dots. Trace the broken lines.

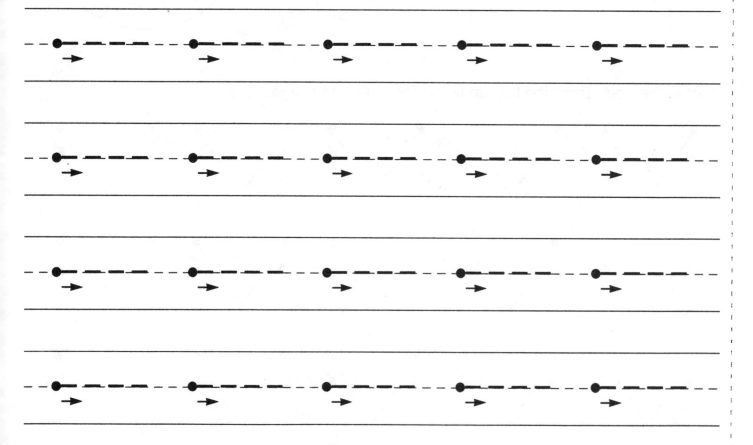

Skills: Fine motor skill development; Eye/hand coordination; Forming horizontal lines

HANDWRITING SKILLS

Follow the direction of each arrow. Then practice writing each letter.

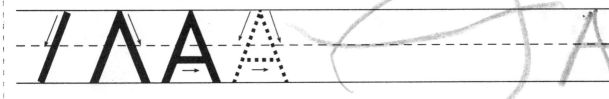

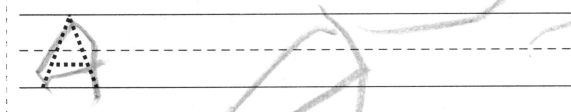

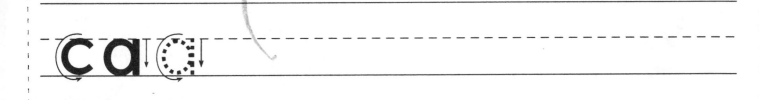

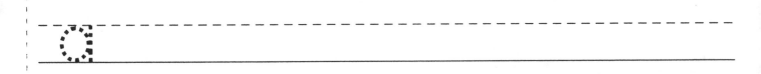

Skills: Forming upper/lowercase "a"; Writing left to right

HANDWRITING SKILLS

Follow the direction of each arrow. Then practice writing each letter.

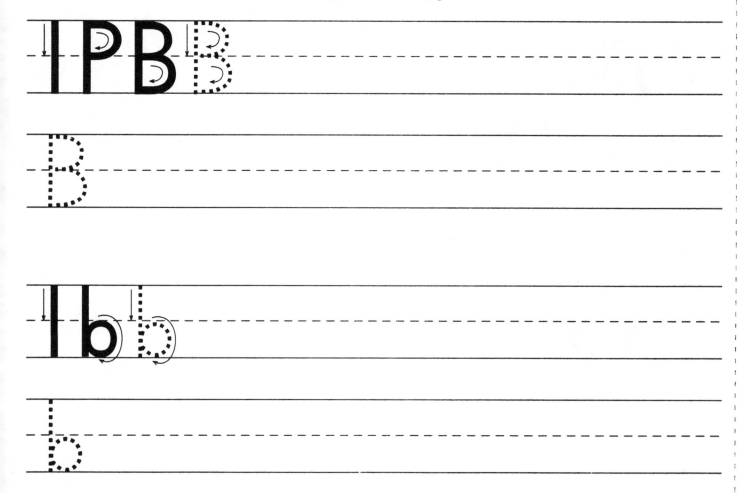

Skills: Forming upper/lowercase "b"; Writing left to right

HANDWRITING SKILLS

Follow the direction of each arrow. Then practice writing each letter.

Skills: Forming upper/lowercase "c"; Writing left to right

HANDWRITING SKILLS

Follow the direction of each arrow. Then practice writing each letter.

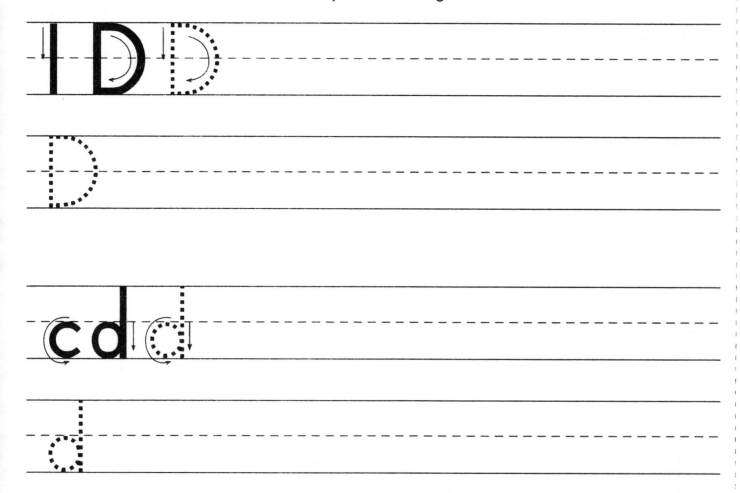

Skills: Forming upper/lowercase "d"; Writing left to right

Follow the direction of each arrow. Then practice writing each letter.

Skills: Forming upper/lowercase "e"; Writing left to right

HANDWRITING SKILLS

Follow the direction of each arrow. Then practice writing each letter.

Skills: Forming upper/lowercase "f"; Writing left to right

HANDWRITING SKILLS

Follow the direction of each arrow. Then practice writing each letter.

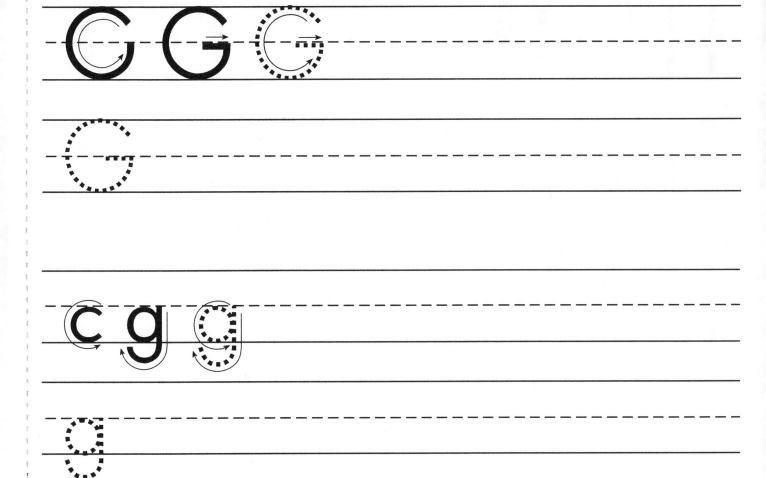

Skills: Forming upper/lowercase "g"; Writing left to right

HANDWRITING SKILLS

Follow the direction of each arrow. Then practice writing each letter.

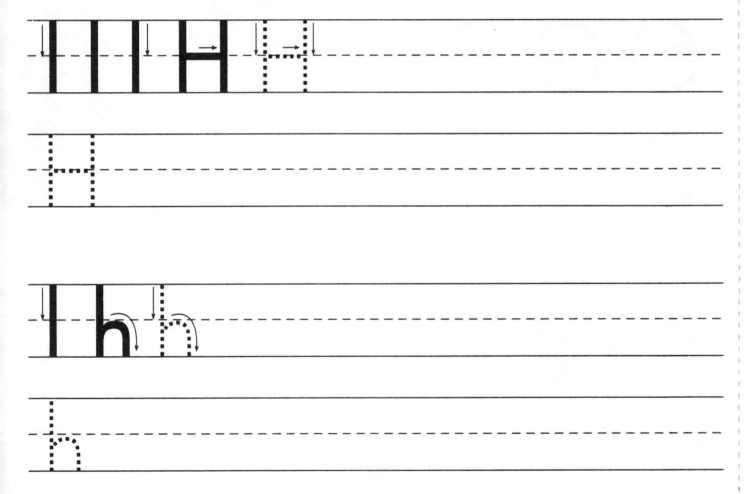

Skills: Forming upper/lowercase "h"; Writing left to right

HANDWRITING SKILLS

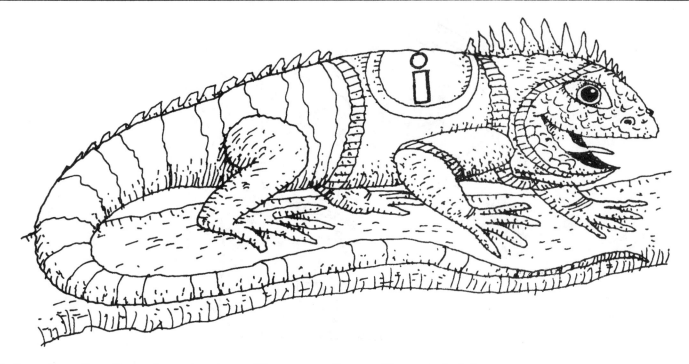

Follow the direction of each arrow. Then practice writing each letter.

Skills: Forming upper/lowercase "i"; Writing left to right

HANDWRITING SKILLS

Follow the direction of each arrow. Then practice writing each letter.

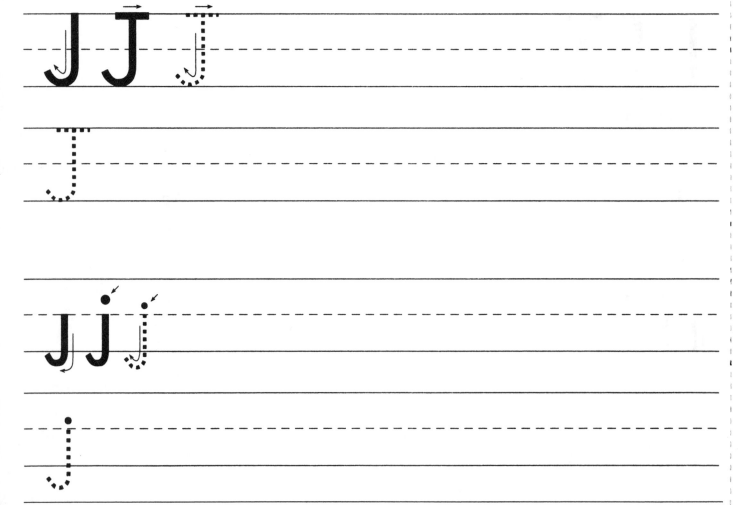

Skills: Forming upper/lowercase "j"; Writing left to right

HANDWRITING SKILLS

Follow the direction of each arrow. Then practice writing each letter.

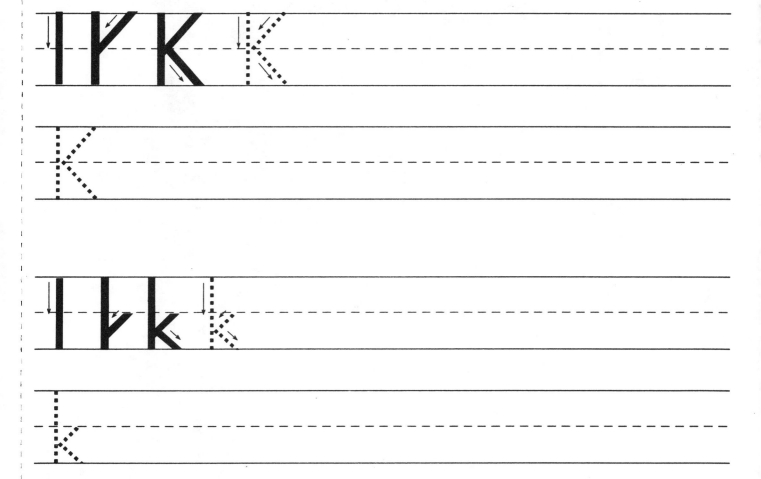

Skills: Forming upper/lowercase "k"; Writing left to right

HANDWRITING SKILLS

Follow the direction of each arrow. Then practice writing each letter.

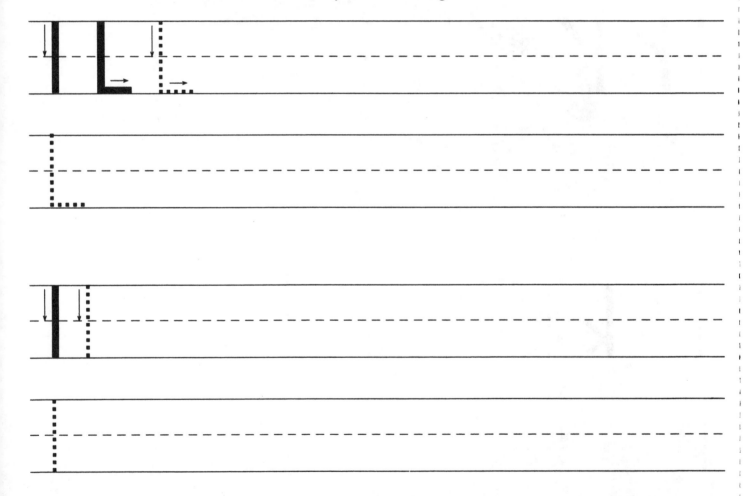

Skills: Forming upper/lowercase "l"; Writing left to right

HANDWRITING SKILLS

Follow the direction of each arrow. Then practice writing each letter.

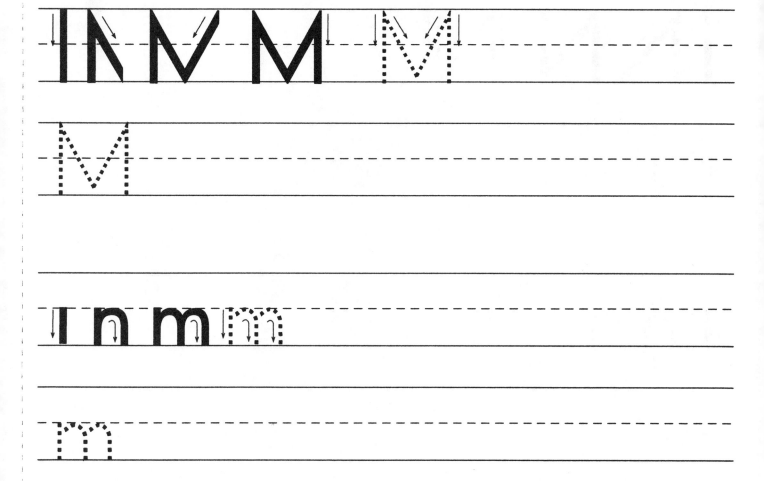

Skills: Forming upper/lowercase "m"; Writing left to right

Follow the direction of each arrow. Then practice writing each letter.

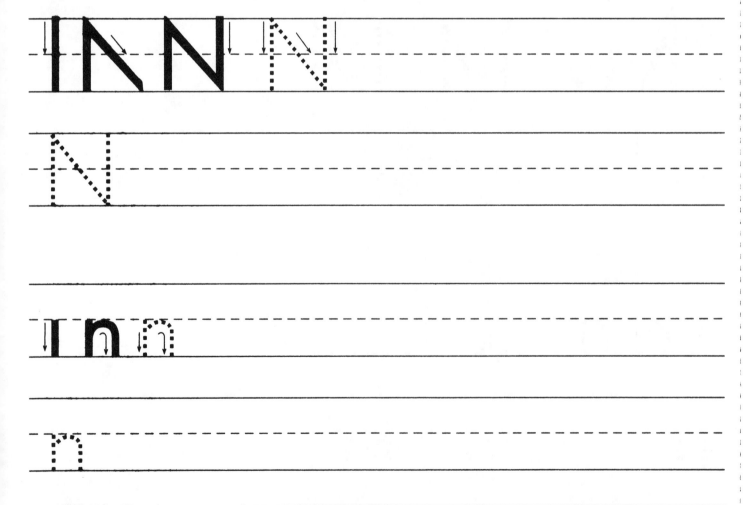

Skills: Forming upper/lowercase "n"; Writing left to right

HANDWRITING SKILLS

Follow the direction of each arrow. Then practice writing each letter.

Skills: Forming upper/lowercase "o"; Writing left to right

Follow the direction of each arrow. Then practice writing each letter.

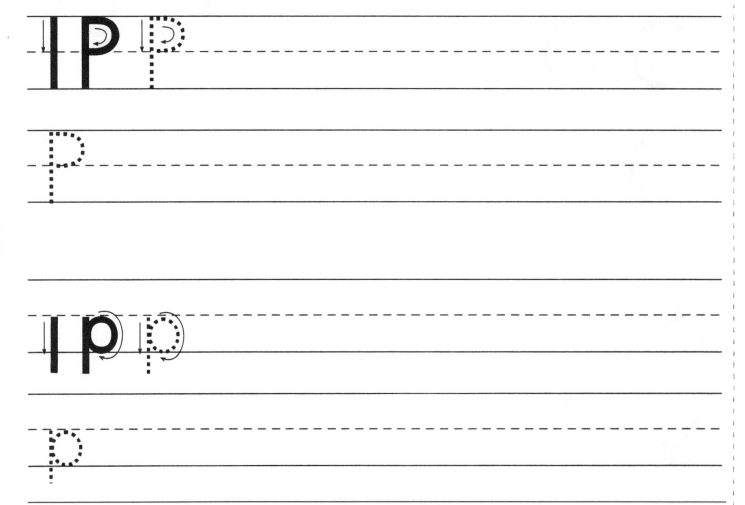

Skills: Forming upper/lowercase "p"; Writing left to right

HANDWRITING SKILLS

Follow the direction of each arrow. Then practice writing each letter.

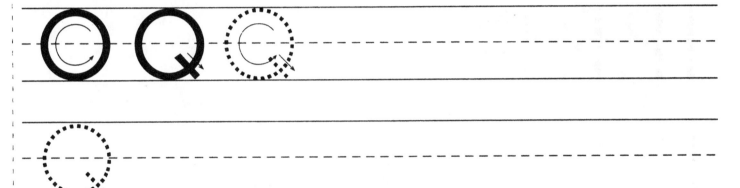

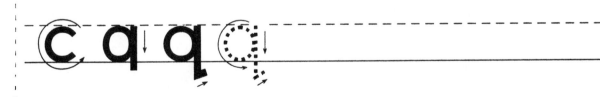

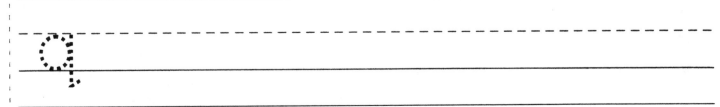

Skills: Forming upper/lowercase "q"; Writing left to right

Follow the direction of each arrow. Then practice writing each letter.

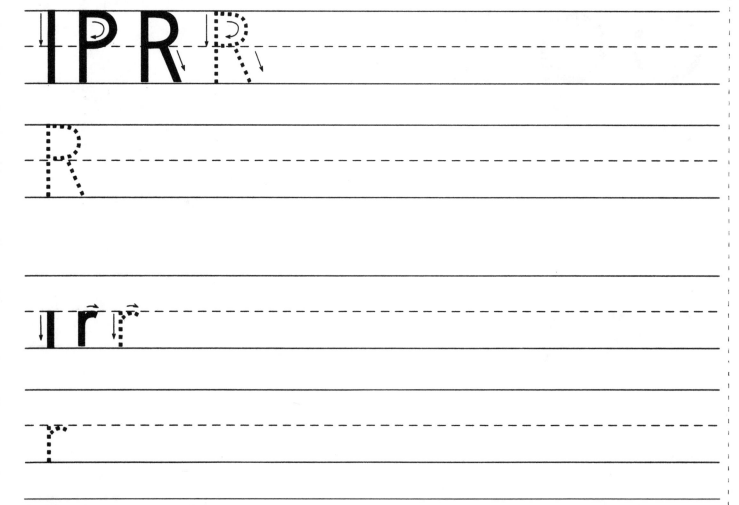

Skills: Forming upper/lowercase "r"; Writing left to right

HANDWRITING SKILLS

Follow the direction of each arrow. Then practice writing each letter.

Skills: Forming upper/lowercase "s"; Writing left to right

HANDWRITING SKILLS

Follow the direction of each arrow. Then practice writing each letter.

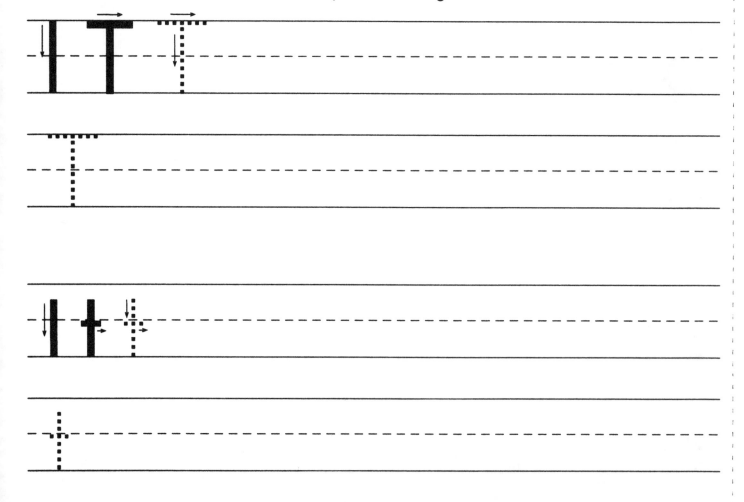

Skills: Forming upper/lowercase "t"; Writing left to right

HANDWRITING SKILLS

Follow the direction of each arrow. Then practice writing each letter.

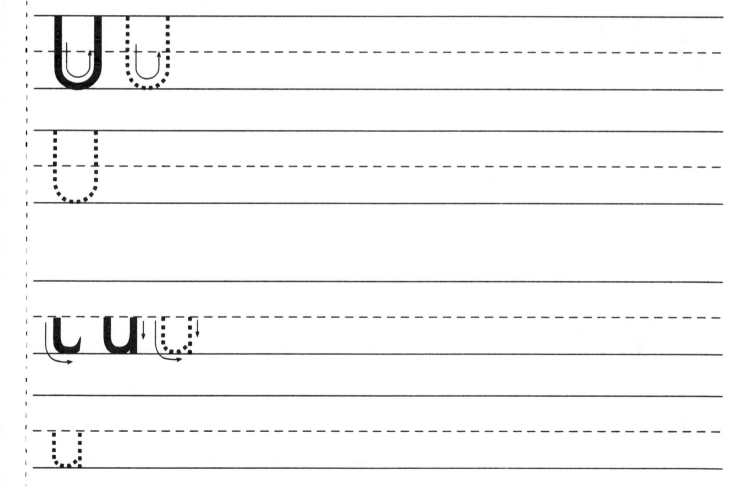

Skills: Forming upper/lowercase "u"; Writing left to right

HANDWRITING SKILLS

Follow the direction of each arrow. Then practice writing each letter.

Skills: Forming upper/lowercase "v"; Writing left to right

Follow the direction of each arrow. Then practice writing each letter.

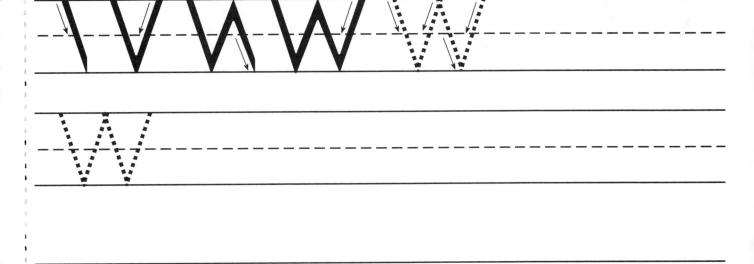

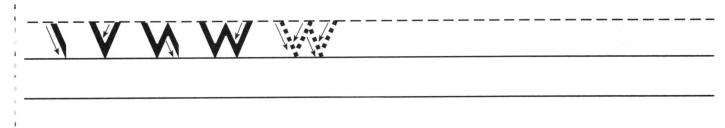

Skills: Forming upper/lowercase "w"; Writing left to right

HANDWRITING SKILLS

Follow the direction of each arrow. Then practice writing each letter.

Skills: Forming upper/lowercase "x"; Writing left to right

Follow the direction of each arrow. Then practice writing each letter.

Skills: Forming upper/lowercase "y"; Writing left to right

Follow the direction of each arrow. Then practice writing each letter.

Skills: Forming upper/lowercase "z"; Writing left to right

HANDWRITING SKILLS

Trace each letter.

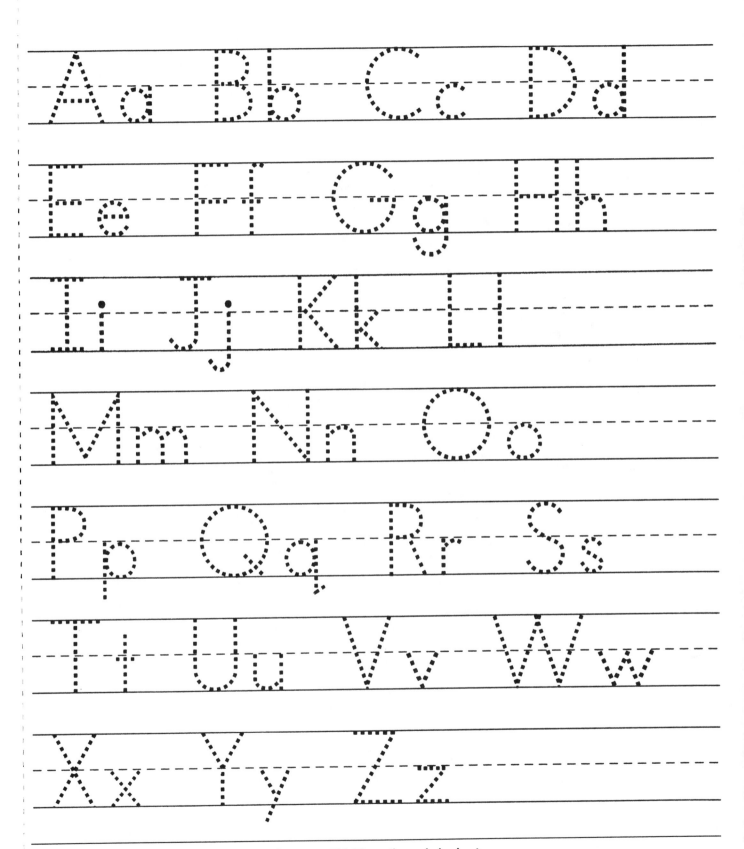

Skills: Forming upper/lowercase letters; Writing the alphabet

HANDWRITING SKILLS

Trace and color the picture.

Skills: Tracing; Fine motor skill development; Eye/hand coordination

HANDWRITING SKILLS

Trace the broken lines.

Skills: Fine motor skill development; Forming vertical and diagonal lines; Eye/hand coordination

red

red

Trace the color word.
Write the color word.
Color these things that are red.

r

Skills: Writing color words; Distinguishing color; Classification; Word recognition

yellow   yellow

Trace the color word.
Write the color word.
Color these things that are yellow.

y

Skills: Writing color words; Distinguishing color; Classification; Word recognition

blue

blue

b

Trace the color word.
Write the color word.
Color these things that are blue.

Skills: Writing color words; Distinguishing color; Classification; Word recognition

orange · orange

Trace the color word.
Write the color word.
Color these things that are orange.

Skills: Writing color words; Distinguishing color; Classification; Word recognition

purple

purple

Trace the color word.
Write the color word.
Color these things that are purple.

p

Skills: Writing color words; Distinguishing color; Classification; Word recognition

green

Trace the color word.
Write the color word.
Color these things that are green.

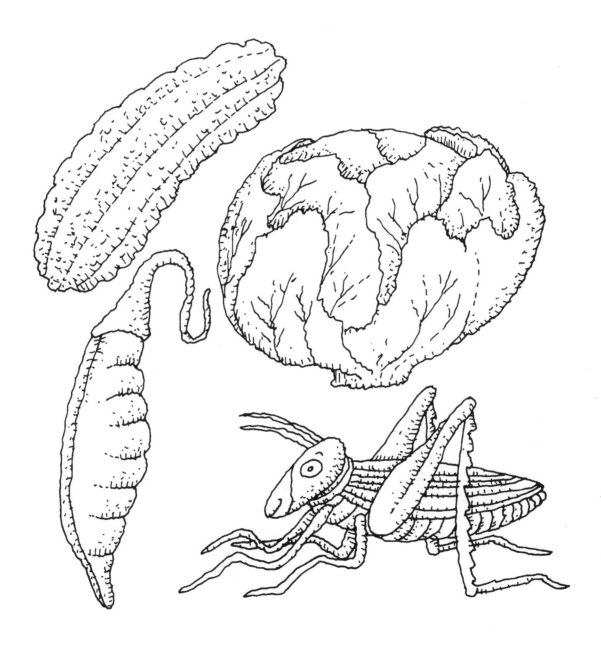

Skills: Writing color words; Distinguishing color; Classification; Word recognition

black

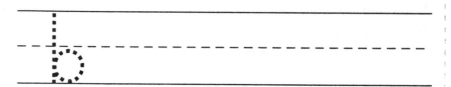

Trace the color word.
Write the color word.
Color these things that are black.

Skills: Writing color words; Distinguishing color; Classification; Word recognition

brown   brown

Trace the color word.
Write the color word.
Color these things that are brown.

Skills: Writing color words; Distinguishing color; Classification; Word recognition

Look at the square.
Then trace, print, and draw.

square

⬜

square

Draw 1 square. Color it blue.

Skills: Fine motor skill development; Sight vocabulary recognition; Association between sight vocabulary and shapes; Shape and color recognition

Look at the circle.
Then trace, print, and draw.

circle

Draw 1 circle. Color it brown.

Skills: Fine motor skill development; Sight vocabulary recognition; Association between sight vocabulary and shapes; Shape and color recognition

Look at the rectangle.
Then trace, print, and draw.

rectangle

rectangle

Draw 1 rectangle. Color it yellow.

Skills: Fine motor skill development; Sight vocabulary recognition; Association between sight vocabulary and shapes; Shape and color recognition

COLORS, SHAPES, AND NUMBERS

Look at the triangle.
Then trace, print, and draw.

triangle

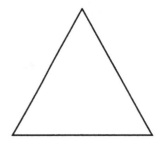

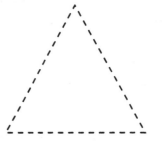

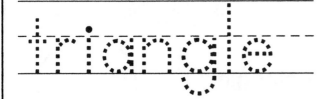

Draw 1 triangle. Color it green.

Skills: Fine motor skill development; Sight vocabulary recognition; Association between sight vocabulary and shapes; Shape and color recognition

COLORS, SHAPES, AND NUMBERS

Match the shape to the word.

Match the word to the shape.

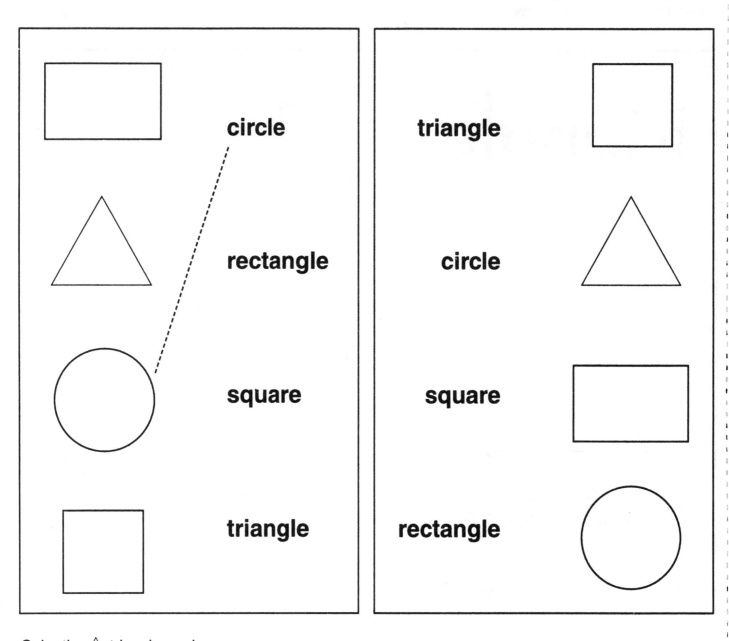

Color the △ triangles red.
Color the ○ circles yellow.
Color the ☐ rectangles green.
Color the ☐ squares blue.

Skills: Following directions; Association between sight vocabulary and shapes; Sight vocabulary recognition; Color recognition

COLORS, SHAPES, AND NUMBERS

Print the word. Color the shape.

square   rectangle   triangle   circle

Skills: Association between sight vocabulary and shapes; Practicing writing skills; Sight vocabulary recognition

COLORS, SHAPES, AND NUMBERS

Circle the correct numeral.

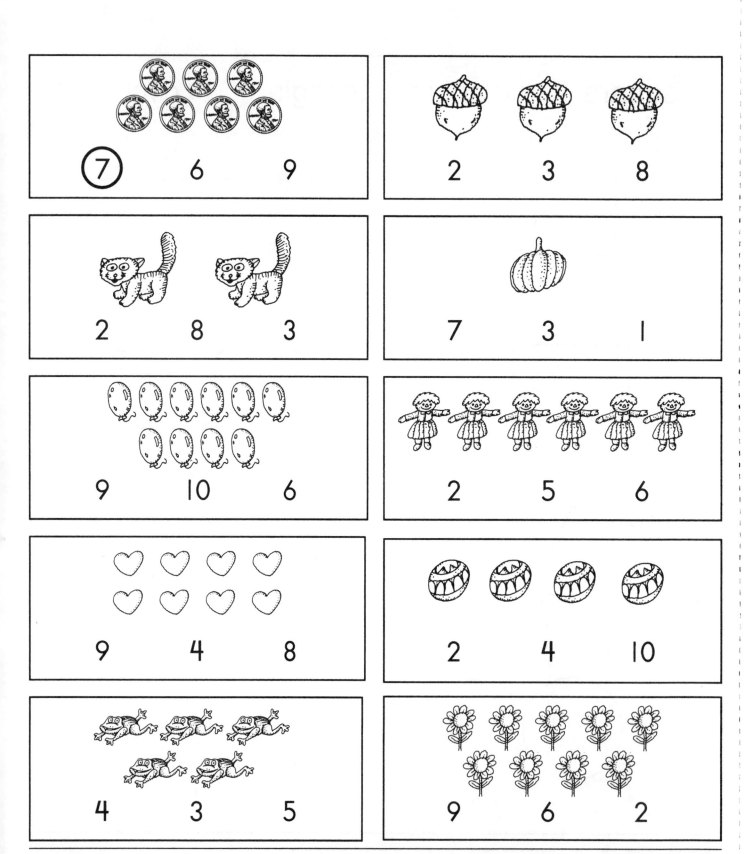

Skills: Recognizing sets of objects and the corresponding numeral; Following directions

COLORS, SHAPES, AND NUMBERS

Print the correct numeral.

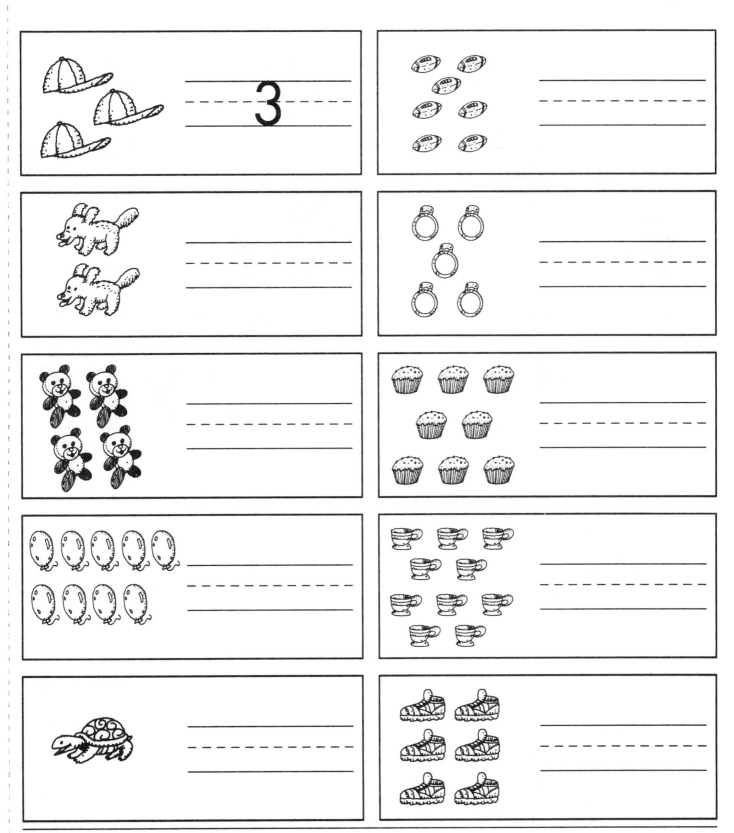

COLORS, SHAPES, AND NUMBERS

Trace and print the words and numerals.

Skills: Recognizing sets of 1 and 2; Association between sight vocabulary, numerals, and sets

COLORS, SHAPES, AND NUMBERS

Trace and print the words and numerals.

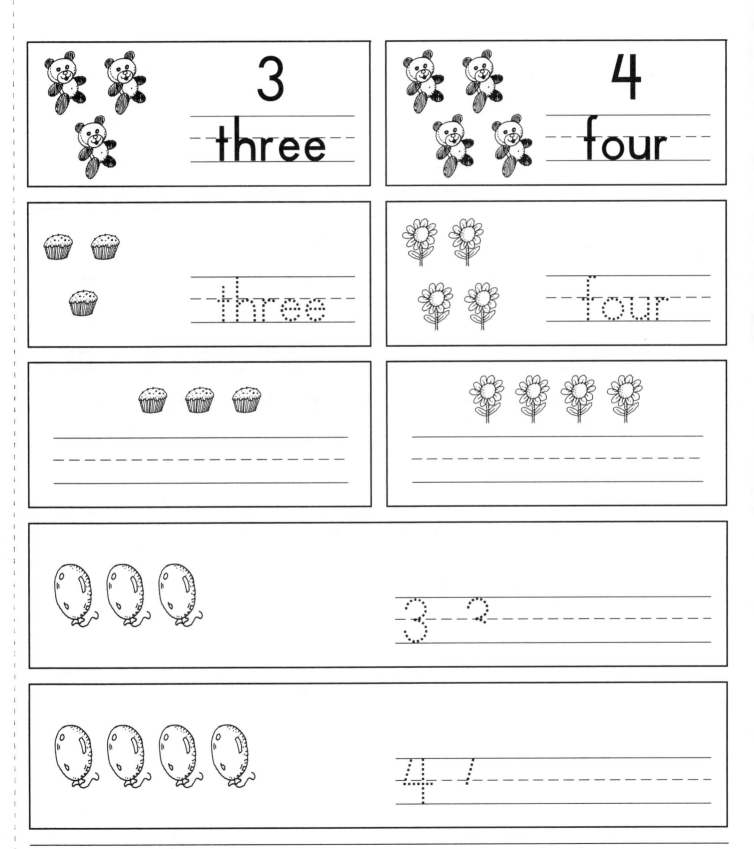

COLORS, SHAPES, AND NUMBERS

Trace and print the words and numerals.

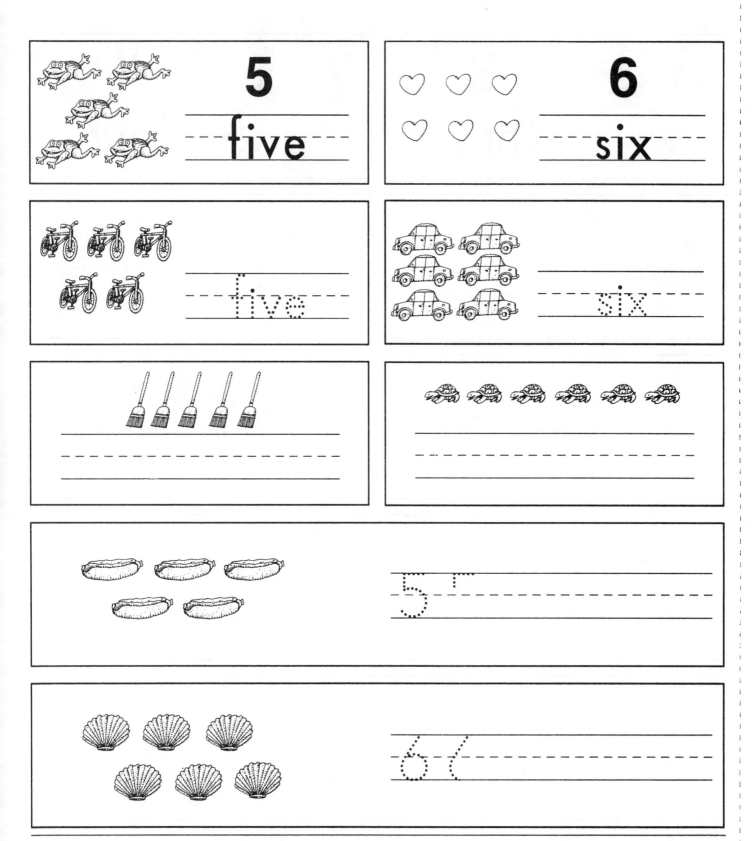

5
five

6
six

five

six

Skills: Recognizing sets of 5 and 6; Association between sight vocabulary, numerals, and sets

COLORS, SHAPES, AND NUMBERS

Trace and print the words and numerals.

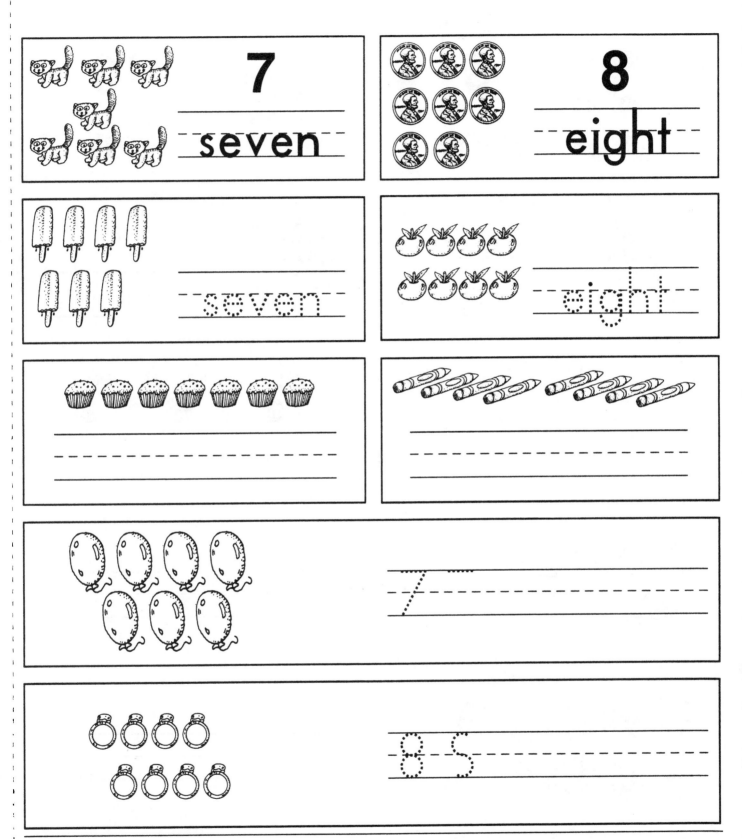

Skills: Recognizing sets of 7 and 8; Association between sight vocabulary, numerals, and sets

COLORS, SHAPES, AND NUMBERS

Trace and print the words and numerals.

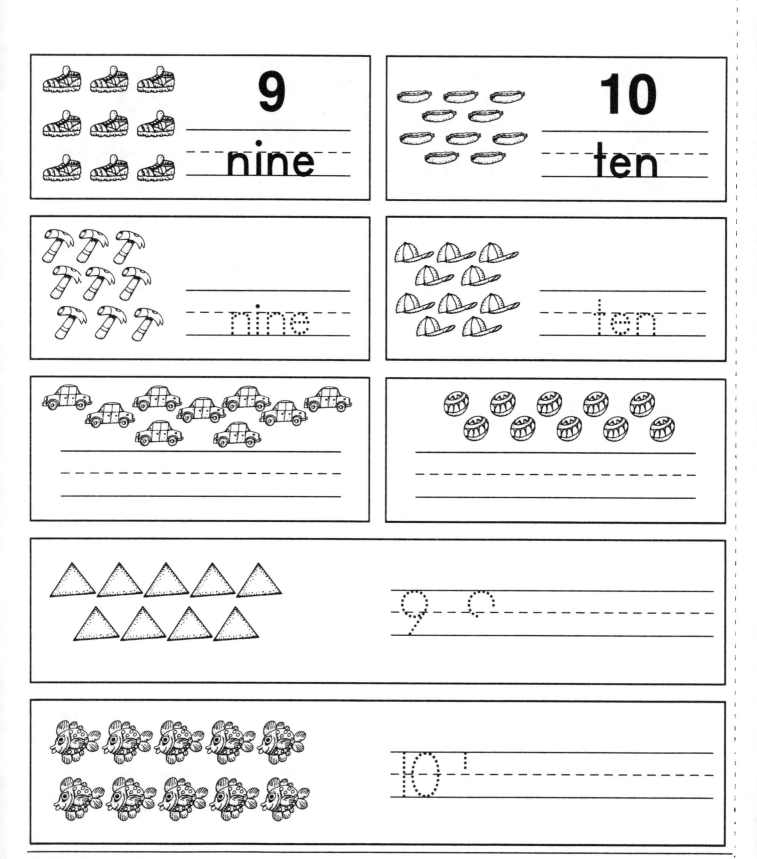

9

nine

10

ten

nine

ten

COLORS, SHAPES, AND NUMBERS

Match the words and numerals.

one	6
two	1
three	8
four	2
five	4
six	3
seven	9
eight	7
nine	5
ten	10

Skills: Recognizing numerals and the corresponding number word

COLORS, SHAPES, AND NUMBERS

Circle the correct word.

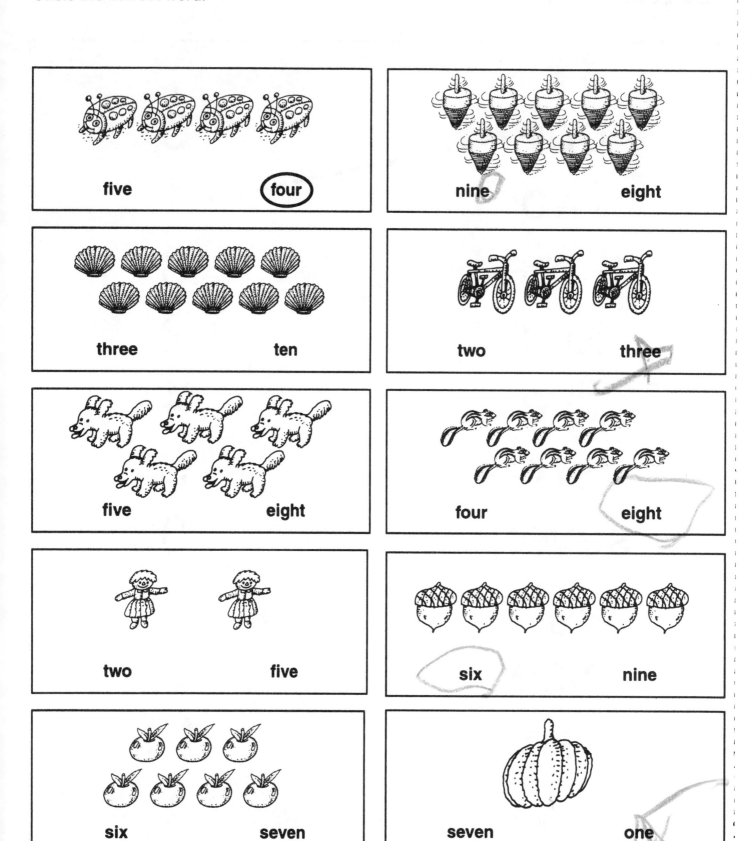

five   (four)

nine   eight

three   ten

two   three

five   eight

four   eight

two   five

six   nine

six   seven

seven   one

Skills: Recognizing sets of objects and the corresponding number word

COLORS, SHAPES, AND NUMBERS

Trace the word. Trace the numeral. Draw the correct number of diamonds.

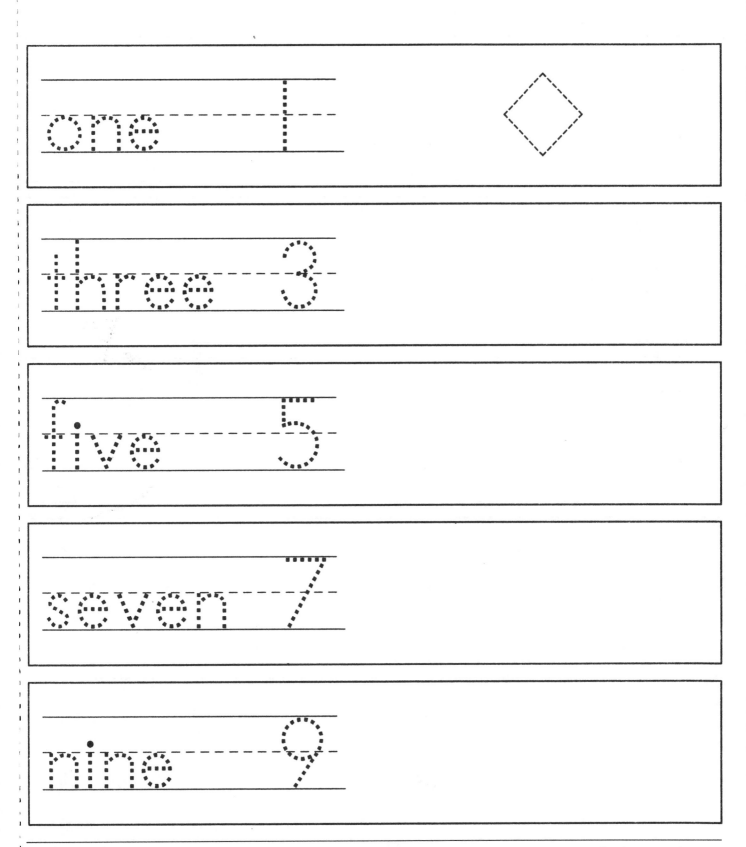

COLORS, SHAPES, AND NUMBERS

Trace the word. Trace the numeral. Draw the correct number of squares.

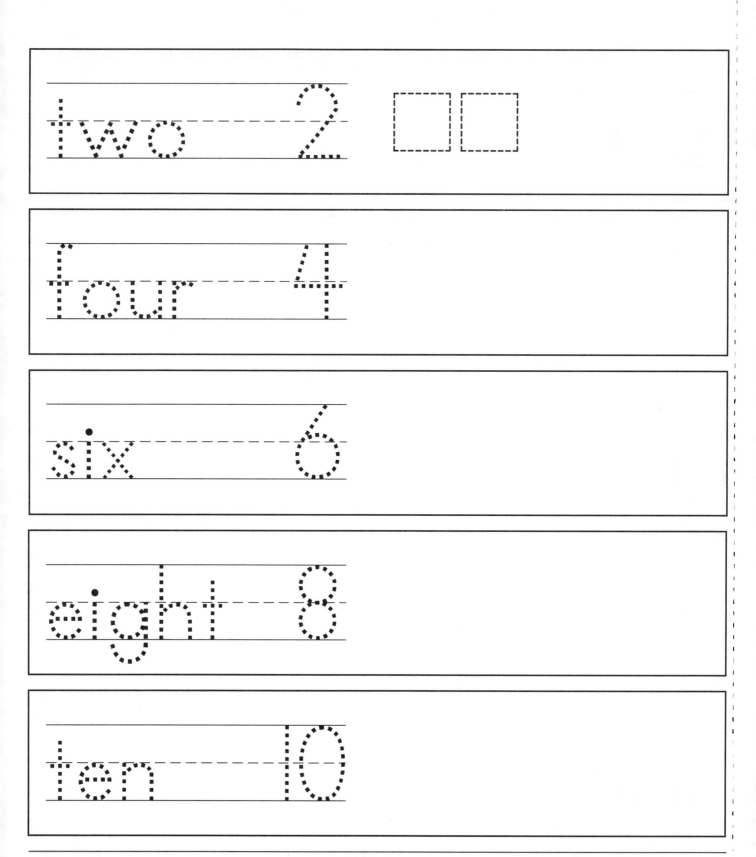

Skills: Recognizing number words and writing numerals; Forming corresponding sets of objects

COLORS, SHAPES, AND NUMBERS

Make 1 green ☐ square.

Make 2 red ◯ circles.

Make 3 blue ☐ rectangles.

Make 4 yellow △ triangles.

Skills: Following directions; Understanding number, shape, and color; Fine motor skill development

COLORS, SHAPES, AND NUMBERS

Color the ○ circles red.

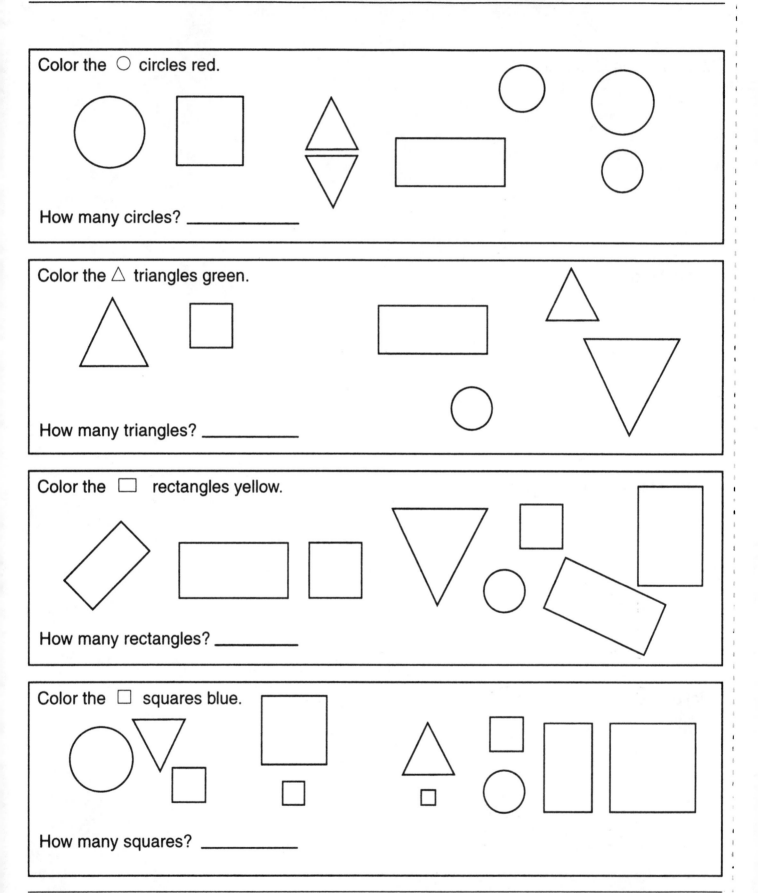

How many circles? _____

Color the △ triangles green.

How many triangles? _____

Color the ▢ rectangles yellow.

How many rectangles? _____

Color the ▢ squares blue.

How many squares? _____

Skills: Following directions; Understanding color, shape, and number; Noticing attributes

PRACTICE PAGE

PRACTICE PAGE

BASIC MATH SKILLS

Look at each butterfly.
What number comes next?

Skills: Ordering numbers to 10; Writing numerals

BASIC MATH SKILLS

Look at each group of cupcakes.
What number comes between?

BASIC MATH SKILLS

Look at the stars.
Write the missing numbers.

Skills: Ordering numbers to 10; Writing numerals

BASIC MATH SKILLS

Look at each picture.
How many are in the first group?

How many are in the second group?
How many in all?

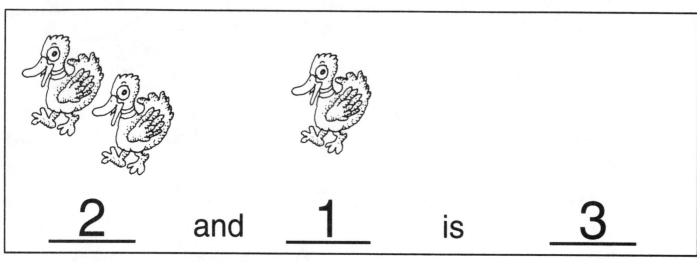

$\underline{\ 2\ }$ and $\underline{\ 1\ }$ is $\underline{\ 3\ }$

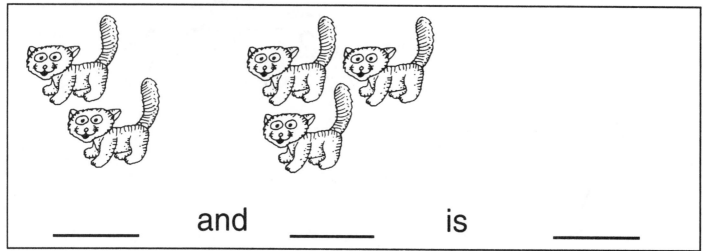

$\underline{\qquad}$ and $\underline{\qquad}$ is $\underline{\qquad}$

$\underline{\qquad}$ and $\underline{\qquad}$ is $\underline{\qquad}$

Skills: Recognizing sets of objects and writing corresponding numerals; Adding groups of objects

BASIC MATH SKILLS

Look at each picture.   How many are in the second group?
How many are in the first group?   How many in all?

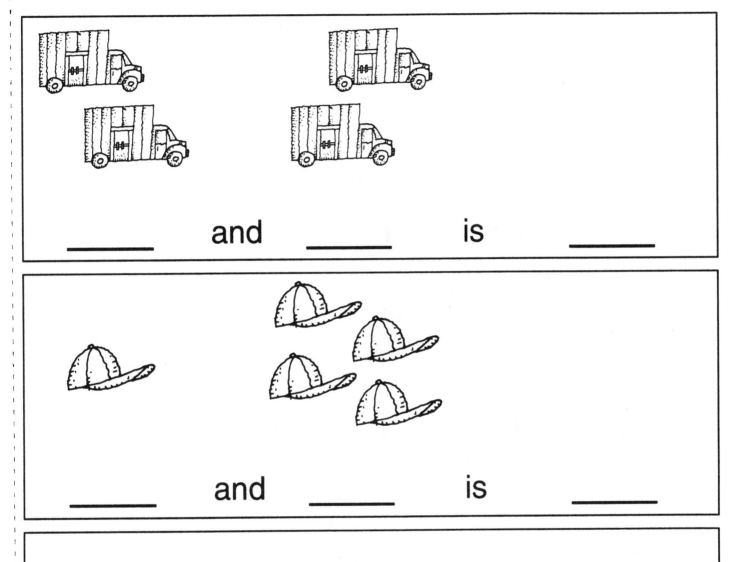

_____   **and**   _____   **is**   _____

_____   **and**   _____   **is**   _____

_____   **and**   _____   **is**   _____

Skills: Recognizing sets of objects and writing corresponding numerals; Adding groups of objects

BASIC MATH SKILLS

Look at each picture.
How many are in the first group?

How many are in the second group?
How many in all?

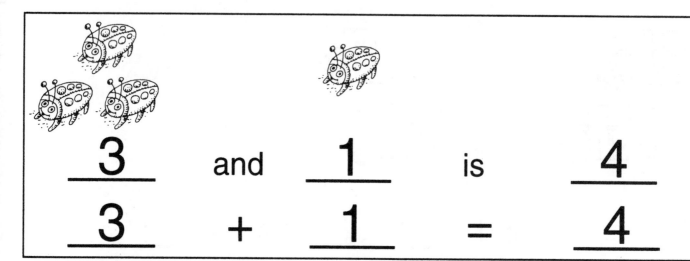

$$\underline{3} \quad \text{and} \quad \underline{1} \quad \text{is} \quad \underline{4}$$

$$\underline{3} \quad + \quad \underline{1} \quad = \quad \underline{4}$$

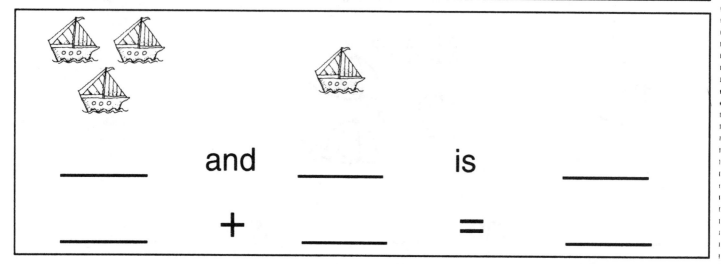

$$\underline{} \quad \text{and} \quad \underline{} \quad \text{is} \quad \underline{}$$

$$\underline{} \quad + \quad \underline{} \quad = \quad \underline{}$$

$$\underline{} \quad \text{and} \quad \underline{} \quad \text{is} \quad \underline{}$$

$$\underline{} \quad + \quad \underline{} \quad = \quad \underline{}$$

Skills: Recognizing sets of objects and writing corresponding numerals; Adding groups of objects; Understanding addition sentences

BASIC MATH SKILLS

Look at each picture.
How many are in the first group?

How many are in the second group?
How many in all?

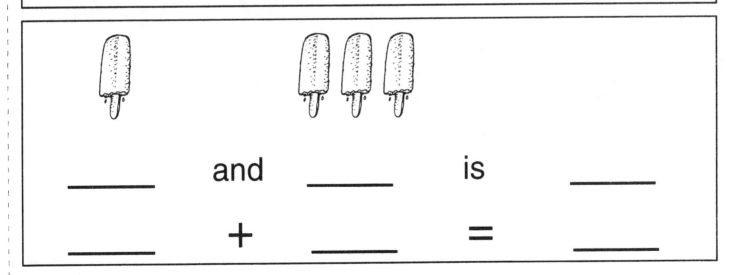

_____ and _____ is _____

_____ + _____ = _____

_____ and _____ is _____

_____ + _____ = _____

_____ and _____ is _____

_____ + _____ = _____

Skills: Recognizing sets of objects and writing corresponding numerals; Adding groups of objects; Understanding addition sentences

BASIC MATH SKILLS

How many in all?
Add to find out.

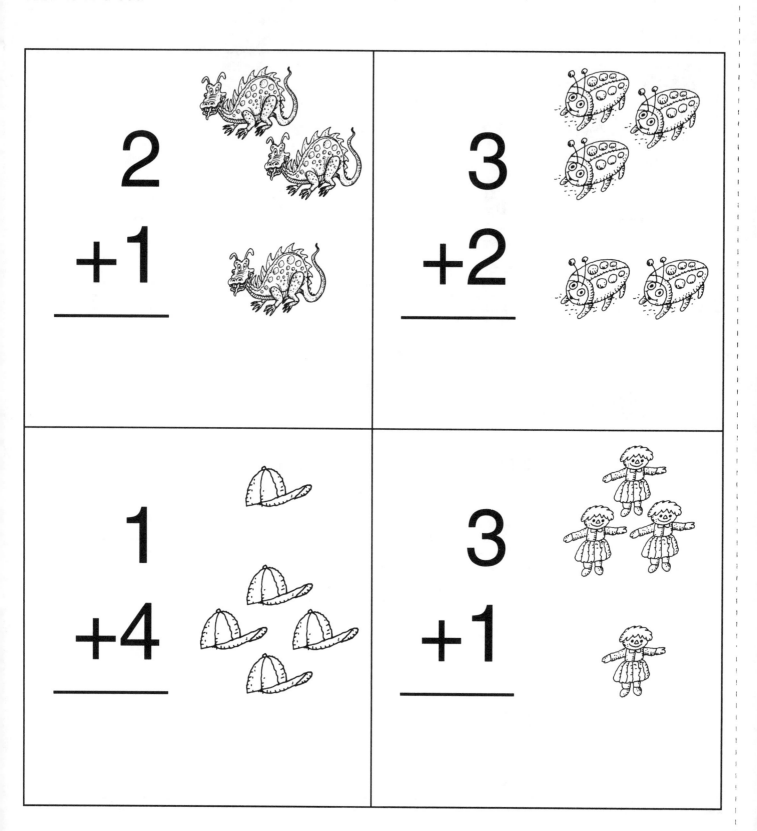

Skills: Solving vertical addition problems; Writing numerals

BASIC MATH SKILLS

How many in all?
Add to find out.

4 + 1 = __

1 + 1 = __

2 + 2 = __

Skills: Solving addition sentences; Writing numerals

BASIC MATH SKILLS

Add the numbers in each sun.
If the answer is 5, color it red.
If the answer is 4, color it blue.
If the answer is 3, color it yellow.

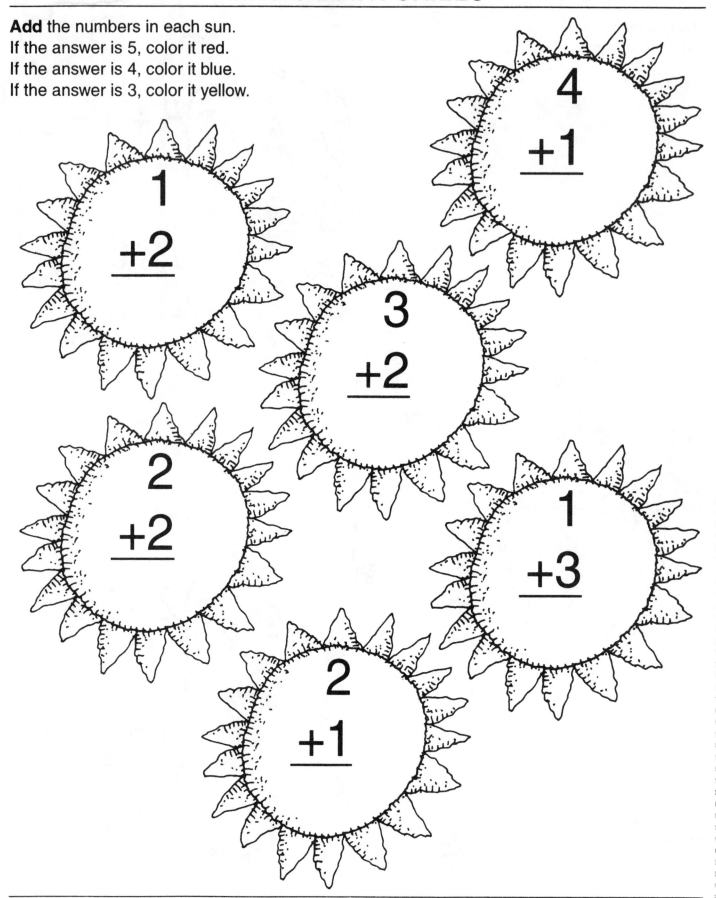

Skills: Solving vertical addition problems; Writing numerals

Add. Then color each picture.

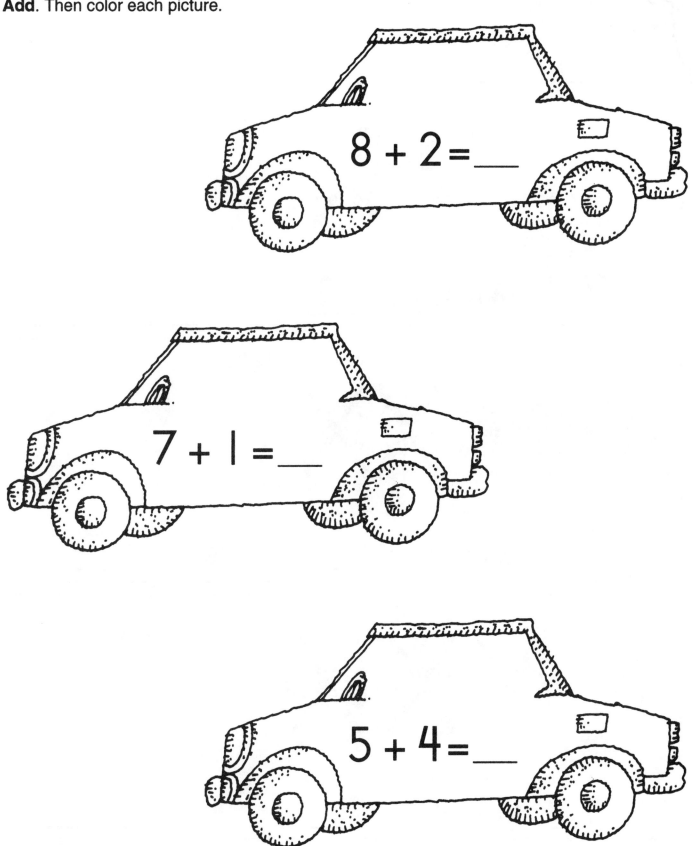

$8 + 2 =$ ___

$7 + 1 =$ ___

$5 + 4 =$ ___

Skills: Solving addition problems; Writing numerals

BASIC MATH SKILLS

Look at each picture.
How many are left?

__3__ take away __1__ is __2__

__5__ take away _____ is _____

__4__ take away _____ is _____

Skills: Recognizing sets of objects and writing corresponding numerals; Subtracting groups of objects

BASIC MATH SKILLS

Look at each picture.
How many are left?

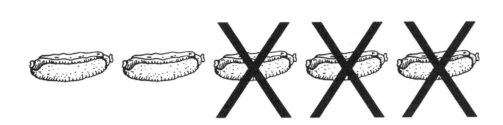

___5___ take away _____ is _____

___4___ take away _____ is _____

___2___ take away _____ is _____

Skills: Recognizing sets of objects and writing corresponding numerals; Subtracting groups of objects

BASIC MATH SKILLS

Look at each picture.
How many are left?

<u> 5 </u> take away <u>   </u> is <u>   </u>

<u> 5 </u> – <u>   </u> = <u>   </u>

<u> 3 </u> take away <u>   </u> is <u>   </u>

<u> 3 </u> – <u>   </u> = <u>   </u>

<u> 4 </u> take away <u>   </u> is <u>   </u>

<u> 4 </u> – <u>   </u> = <u>   </u>

Skills: Recognizing sets of objects and writing corresponding numerals; Subtracting groups of objects; Understanding subtraction sentences

BASIC MATH SKILLS

Look at each picture.
How many are left?

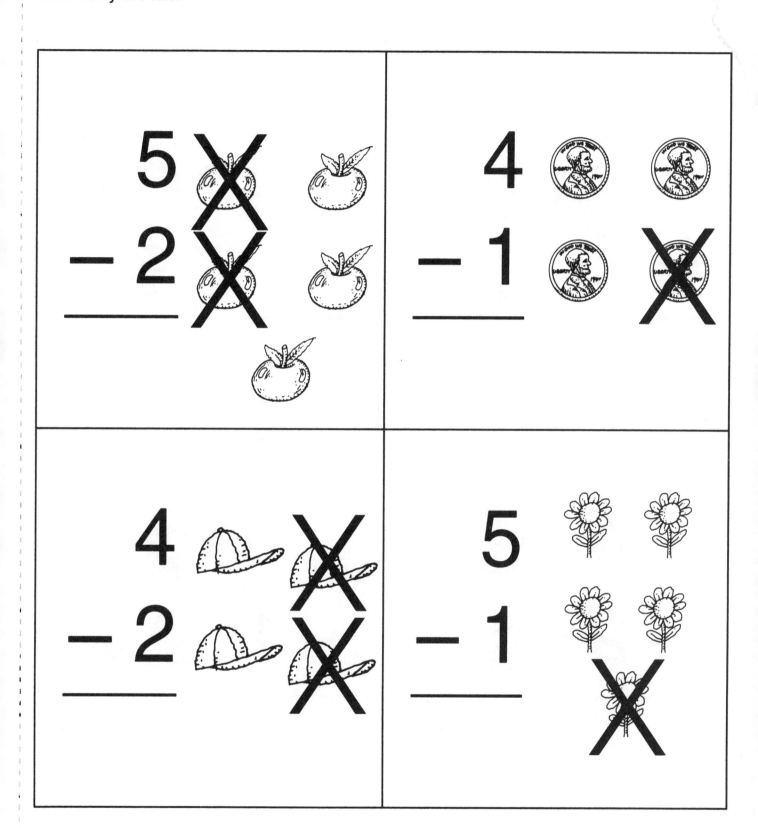

Skills: Solving vertical subtraction problems; Writing numerals

BASIC MATH SKILLS

Look at each picture.
How many are left?

$$\begin{array}{r} 5 \\ -\ 2 \\ \hline \end{array}$$

$$\begin{array}{r} 4 \\ -\ 1 \\ \hline \end{array}$$

$$\begin{array}{r} 4 \\ -\ 2 \\ \hline \end{array}$$

$$\begin{array}{r} 5 \\ -\ 1 \\ \hline \end{array}$$

Skills: Solving vertical subtraction problems; Writing numerals

BASIC MATH SKILLS

Subtract the numbers in each heart.
If the answer is **1**, color it red.
If the answer is **2**, color it yellow.
If the answer is **3**, color it green.

BASIC MATH SKILLS

Follow the dots from **1** to **25** to find a furry friend.

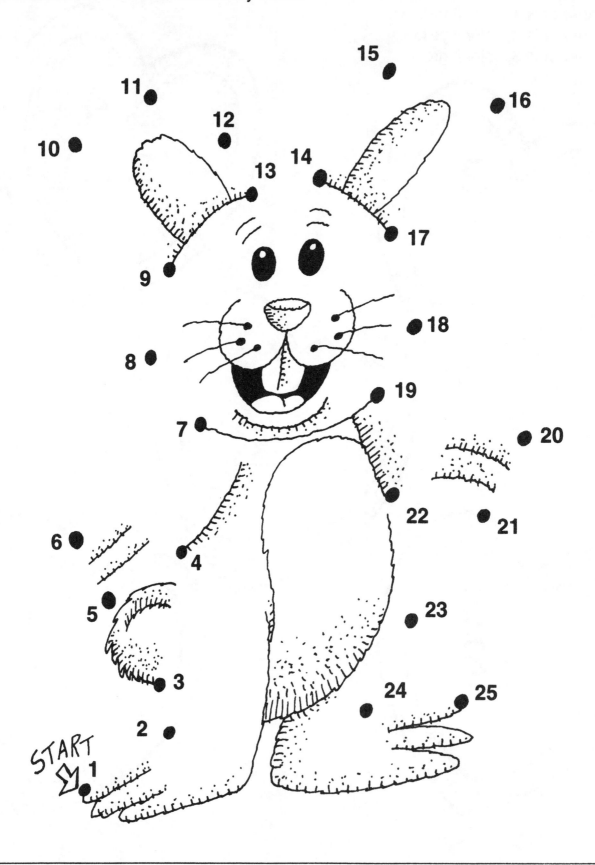

Skills: Ordering numerals from one to twenty-five; Following directions

BASIC MATH SKILLS

Look at these footballs.
Make groups of **ten**.

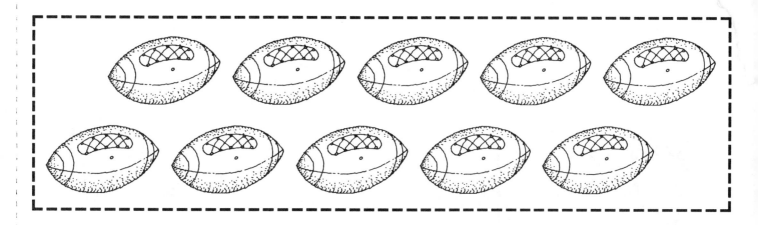

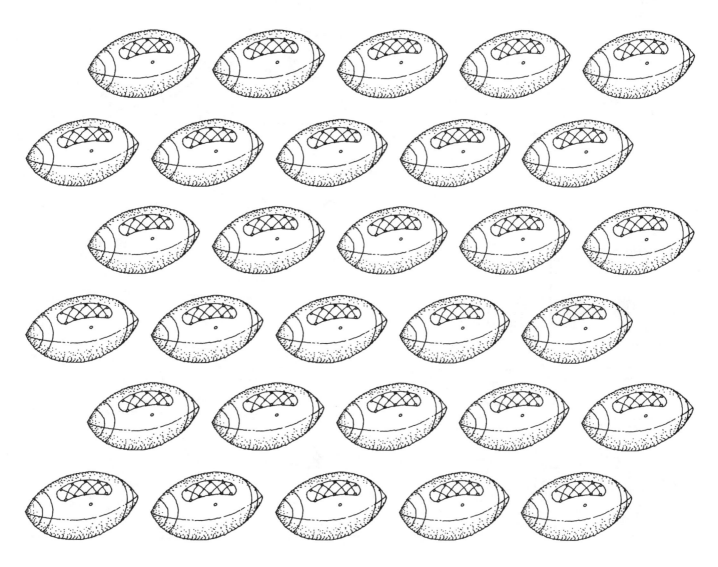

Skills: Forming groups of ten; Counting objects to form groups

BASIC MATH SKILLS

Watch the train race down the track.
How many circles do you see?
Put an **X** on each one.

Skills: Identifying circles; Counting

BASIC MATH SKILLS

Which path leads to the pond?
Is it the one with **squares** or the one with **circles**?
Find out by leading the duck to the pond.

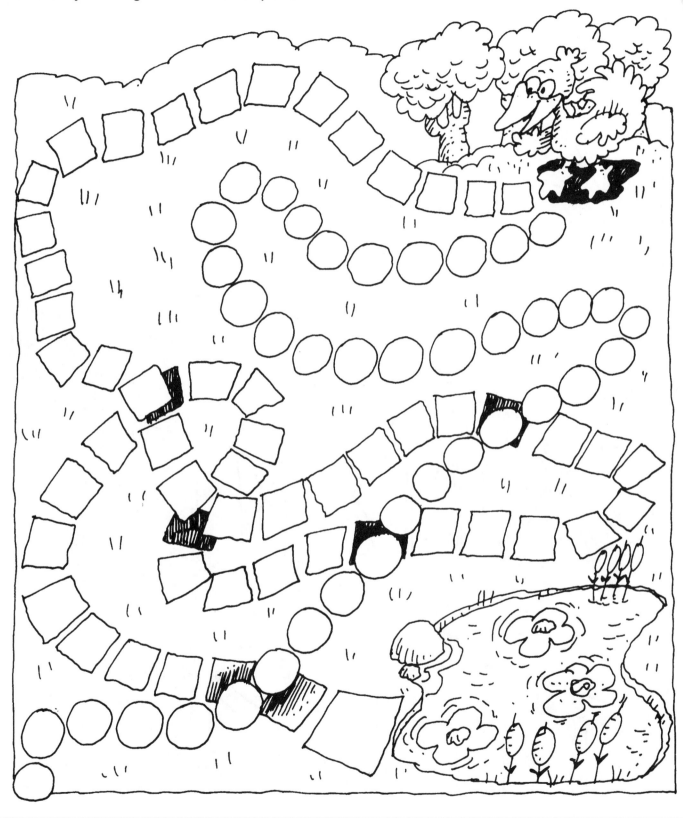

Skills: Identifying squares and circles

BASIC MATH SKILLS

Let's visit the farm.
How many **triangles** do you see?
Put an **X** on each one.

Skills: Identifying triangles; Counting

BASIC MATH SKILLS

The children are building a fortress.
Help them build it.
Color all the **rectangles** you see red.
Color the rest of the shapes blue.

Skills: Identifying rectangles

BASIC MATH SKILLS

Look at the pattern in each row.
Draw shapes to continue each pattern.

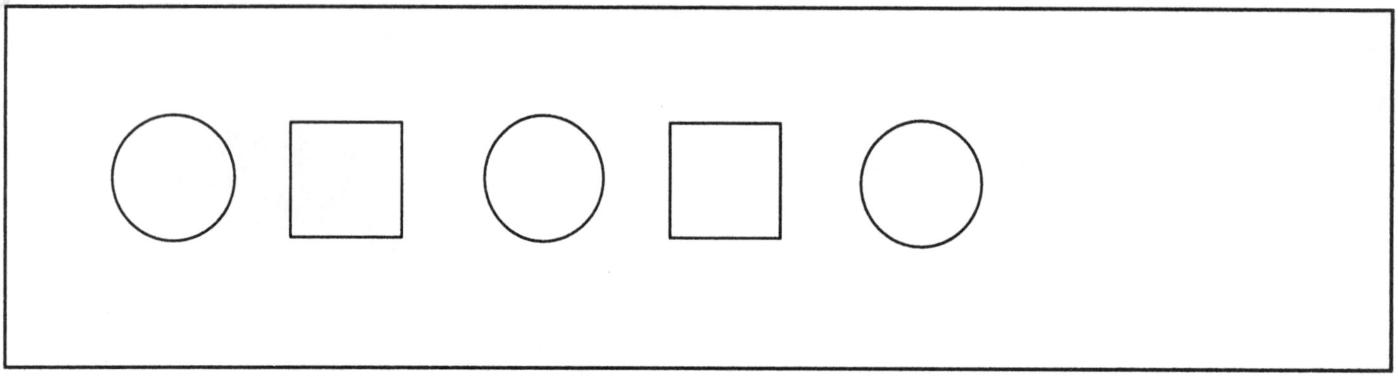

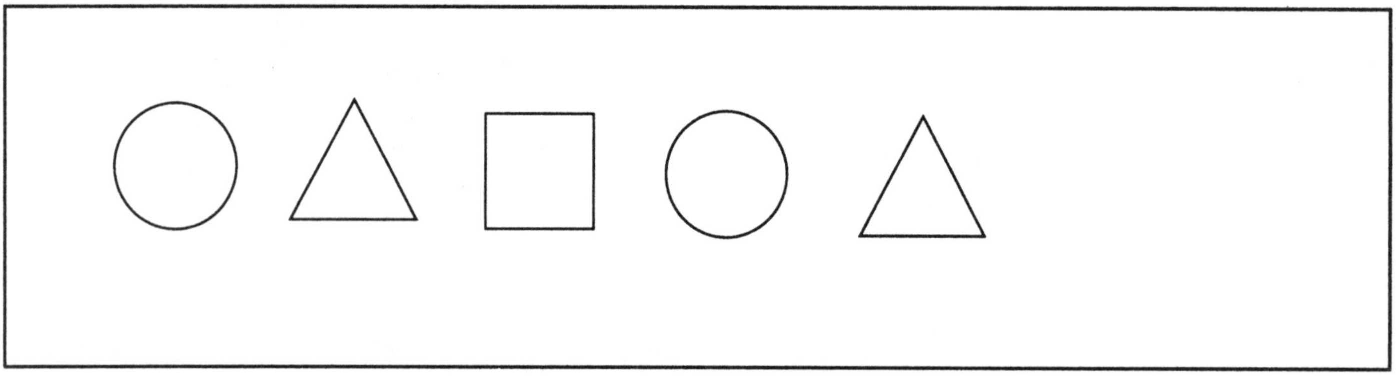

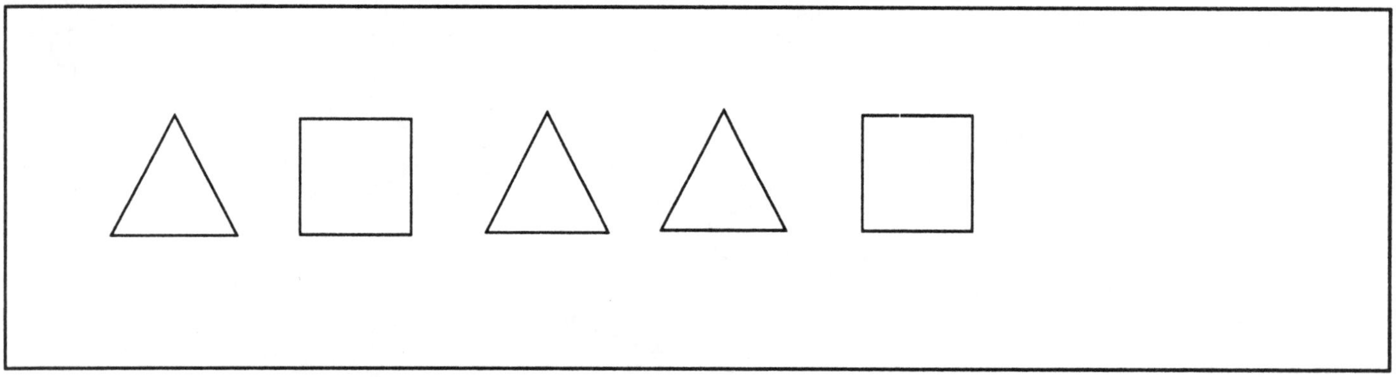

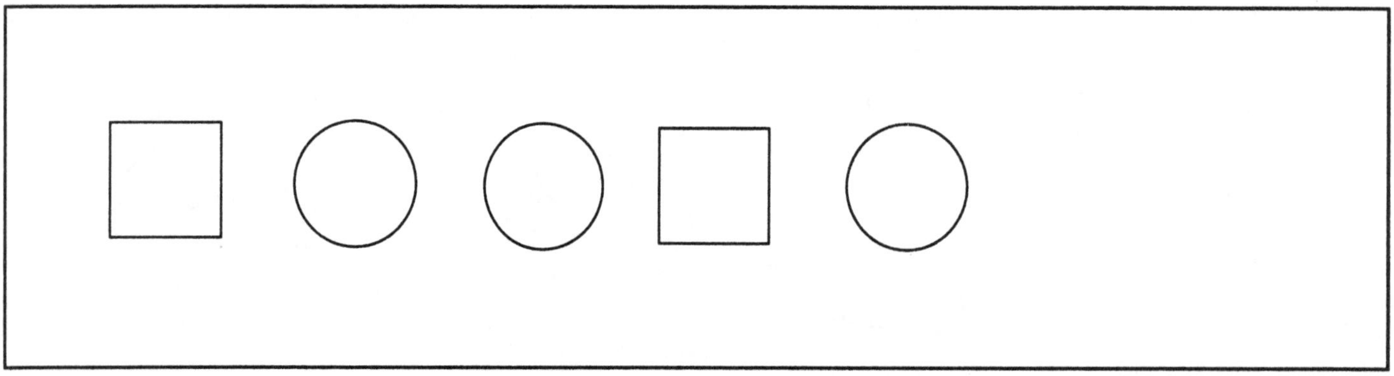

○ □ ○ □ ○

○ △ □ ○ △

△ □ △ △ □

□ ○ ○ □ ○

Skills: Observing and continuing patterns

BASIC MATH SKILLS

Let's play ball!
How many sports can you play?
Look at the pattern in each row.
Draw a circle around the picture that continues each pattern.

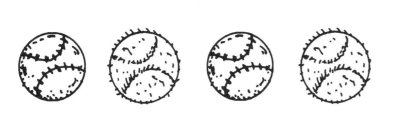

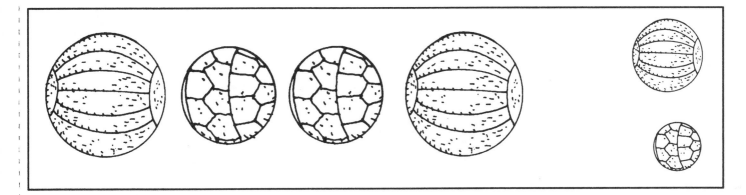

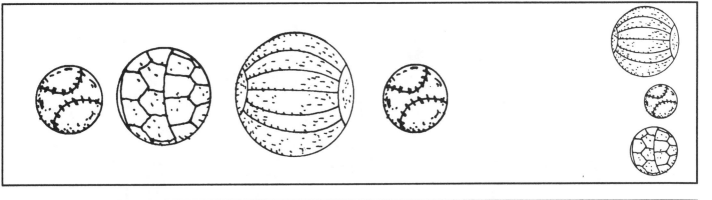

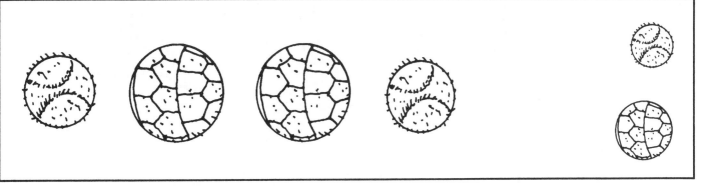

Skills: Observing and continuing patterns

BASIC MATH SKILLS

Every child wants a balloon.
Draw a line to connect each child with a balloon.

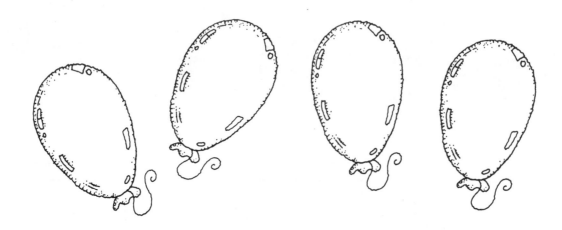

Skills: One-to-one correspondence; Matching

BASIC MATH SKILLS

Look at the first table.
Count the number in each set of cupcakes.
Then look at the second table.
Count the number in each set of cupcakes.
Then draw lines to connect the sets with the same number of cupcakes.

Skills: Identifying sets; Matching

BASIC MATH SKILLS

The kitten got into the jam.
Look what he did to the chairs.
Color the chair that shows more paw prints than the other chair.

Skills: Identifying sets; Understanding more than

BASIC MATH SKILLS

Look at the dots inside each balloon.
Color the balloon that shows 2 dots blue.
Color the balloon that shows 4 dots green.
Color the balloon that shows 6 dots yellow.
Color the balloon that shows 8 dots orange.
Color the balloon that shows 10 dots red.

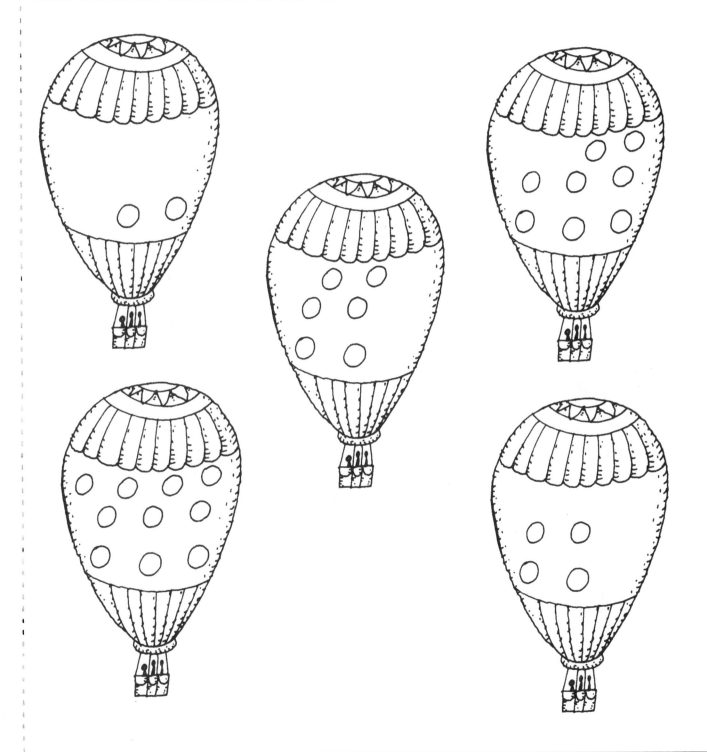

Skills: Counting; Identifying sets

BASIC MATH SKILLS

We need to get supplies for school!
Look at the numbers on the left.
Look at the supplies on the rest of the page.
Count the number of school supplies in each group.
Draw a line to connect each numeral with the correct number of supplies.

1

3

5

7

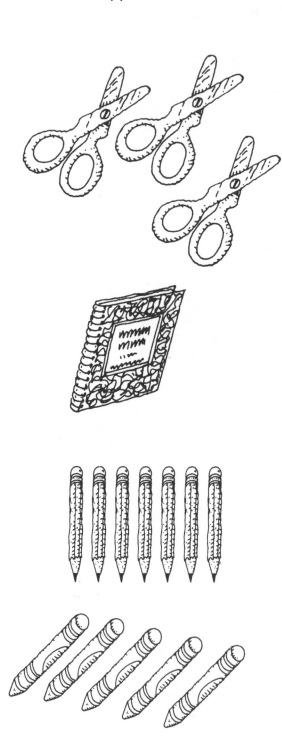

Skills: Counting; Identifying sets; Recognizing numerals

BASIC MATH SKILLS

Let's go to the supermarket.
Look at each numeral and the picture next to it on the grocery list.
Circle that number of things at the supermarket.

Skills: Creating sets of objects; Recognizing numerals; Counting

BASIC MATH SKILLS

Let's have a party!
Look at each numeral and the picture next to it on the party list.
Circle that number of things at the party store.

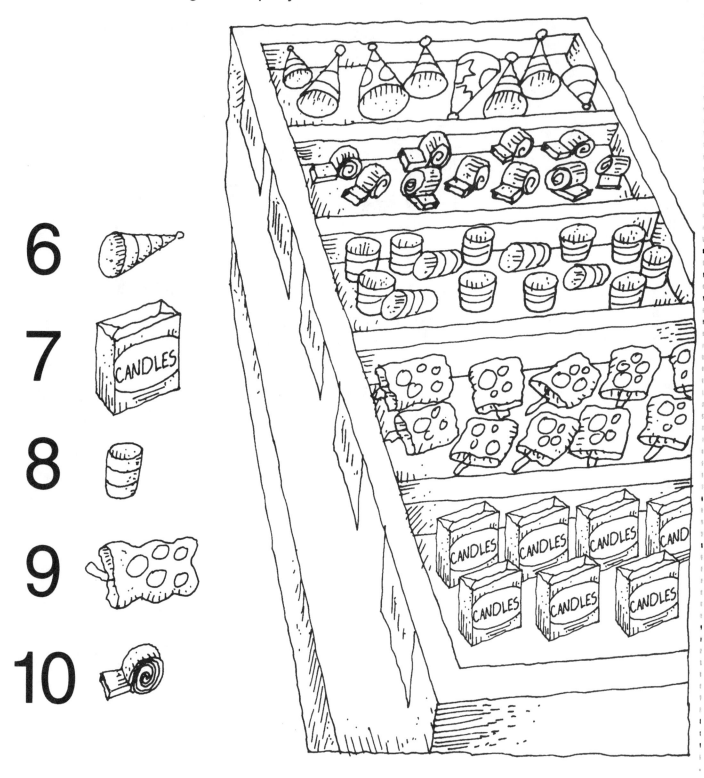

6

7 CANDLES

8

9

10

Skills: Creating sets of objects; Recognizing numerals; Counting

BASIC MATH SKILLS

Who's that riding on the pony?
Follow the dots from **1** to **25** to find out.
Then finish coloring the picture.

Skills: Number order; Recognizing numerals

BASIC MATH SKILLS

Where is the sea lion?
Follow the dots from **1** to **50** to find out.
Then finish coloring the picture.

Skills: Number order; Recognizing numerals

BASIC MATH SKILLS

Watch the farmer bring in his crop!
Use the color code to finish the picture.

Color: 1 = red   2 = orange   7 = brown
        3 = green   4 = yellow
        5 = blue   6 = black

Skills: Recognizing numerals; Matching numerals to color codes

BASIC MATH SKILLS

Let's go to the playground!
Follow the numbers down the path to get to the playground.
Begin at 1.
Trace each number.

Skills: Recognizing numerals

BASIC MATH SKILLS

How many cupcakes did we make?
Count them.
Write one number on each cupcake, from **1** to **12**.

Skills: Counting; Writing numerals from 1 to 12

BASIC MATH SKILLS

Look at the train.
Circle the **first** car.
Draw a **line** under the **second** car.
Put an **X** on the **third** car.

Skills: Recognizing ordinal numbers; Developing vocabulary

BASIC MATH SKILLS

What a long chain of flowers!
Color the **first**, **second** and **third** flowers blue.
Color the **fourth**, **fifth** and **sixth** flowers red.
Color the **seventh**, **eighth** and **ninth** flowers green.
Color the **tenth** flower any color you wish.

START

Skills: Recognizing ordinal numbers; Developing vocabulary

BASIC MATH SKILLS

What fun!
Find and circle the numbers **1** through **10** hidden in this picture.

Skills: Counting; Recognizing numerals

BASIC MATH SKILLS

Drive the cart through the course and look for numbers.
Find and circle the numbers **1** through **10** hidden in this picture.

Skills: Counting; Recognizing numerals

BASIC MATH SKILLS

Play teddy bear bingo with a friend.
Use the teddy bear on this page.
Your friend can use the one on the
following page.

You'll need: 1 pair of dice
scraps of paper

The first player rolls the dice and covers the number rolled
on his teddy bear with a scrap of paper.
Then the second player rolls and covers the number rolled
on her teddy bear with a scrap of paper.
If a number is already covered, you skip a turn.
The winner is the player who covers all his teddy bear's numbers first.

Skills: Counting; Matching; Identifying numbers to 10

BASIC MATH SKILLS

Use this teddy bear
to play teddy bear bingo.

Skills: Counting; Matching; Identifying numbers to 10

BASIC MATH SKILLS

Look at the numbers on the cupcakes.
Write the missing numbers.

Skills: Ordering numbers; Writing numbers

BASIC MATH SKILLS

Here comes the mail carrier!
He needs to put the **small** packages in the **top** sack
and the **large** packages in the **bottom** sack.
Draw lines to connect each package to its right sack.

Skills: Developing vocabulary; Making comparisons

BASIC MATH SKILLS

Look at the numbers on the turtle's back.
Color all the numbers that are **greater than** 5 blue.
Color all the numbers that are **less than** 5 red.

Skills: Recognizing numbers; Understanding greater than and less than; Making comparisons

BASIC MATH SKILLS

Look what the fishermen caught!
Look at the numbers in each pair of fish.
Color the fish with the **greater** number **orange**.
Color the fish with the **lesser** number **yellow**.

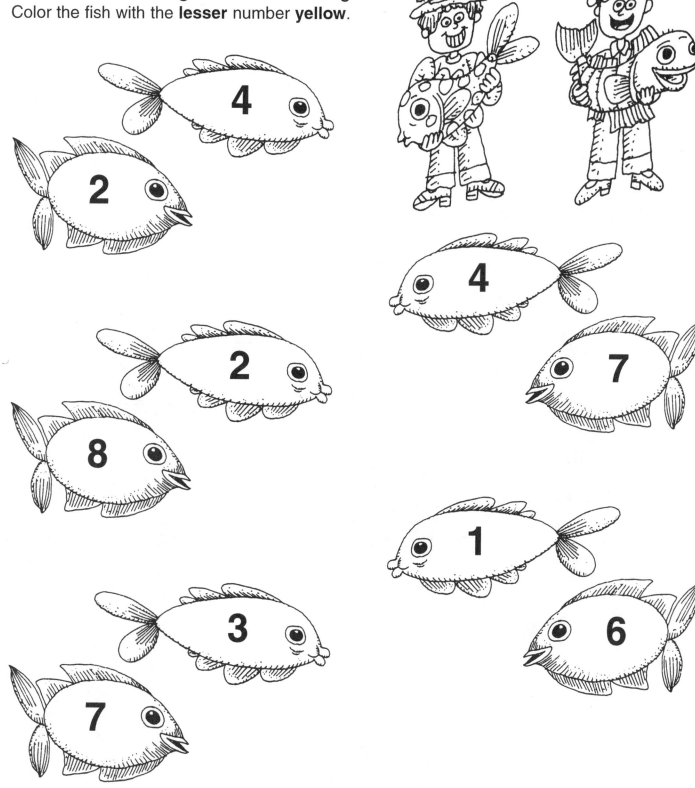

Skills: Recognizing numbers; Understanding greater than and less than

BASIC MATH SKILLS

Look at the pairs of things around the island and in the sea.
Circle the **lighter** one.
Put an **X** on the **heavier** one.

Skills: Developing vocabulary; Comparing weight; Thinking critically

BASIC MATH SKILLS

Look at the pair in each box.
Circle the **shorter** one.
Put an **X** on the **taller** one.

Skills: Developing vocabulary; Comparing height

BASIC MATH SKILLS

Everyone is going to the carousel.
Which path should they take?
Look at each set of paths.
Trace the path that is **shorter**.
Cross out the path that is **longer**.

Skills: Developing vocabulary; Comparing length

BASIC MATH SKILLS

Look at the toys next to each child
Circle the one that is **shorter**.
Put an **X** on the one that is **longer**.

Skills: Developing vocabulary; Comparing length

BASIC MATH SKILLS

The fishermen are using a fish to measure.
Help them find out the length of each object.
Look at the pictures.
Count how many fish lengths long it is.
Then write the numeral on the line.

Measuring fish

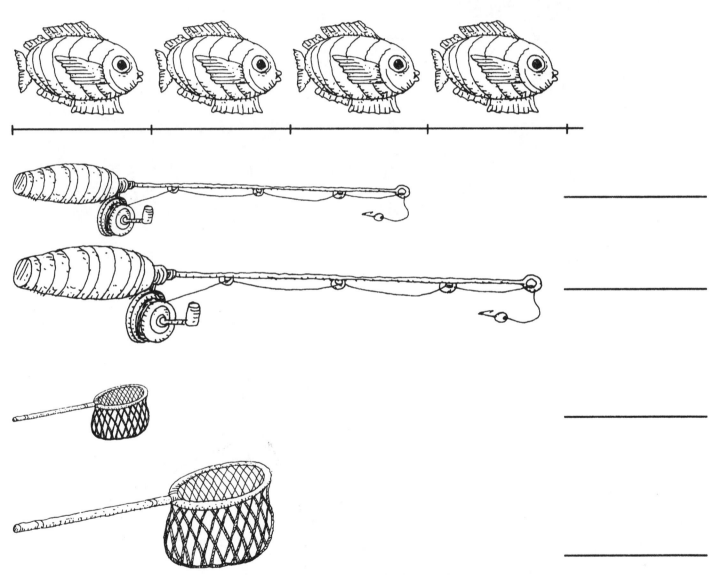

_____

_____

_____

_____

Skills: Measuring length; Counting; Writing numerals

BASIC MATH SKILLS

The bear is using his paw prints to measure.
Help him find out the length of each object.
Look at the pictures.
Count how many paw prints long it is.
Then write the numeral on the line.

Measuring paws

Skills: Measuring length; Counting; Writing numerals

BASIC MATH SKILLS

The farmer is measuring his squash.
Help him find the length of each squash.
Look at each one.
Count and trace the numbers to show how many squares long it is.
Then write the numeral on the line.

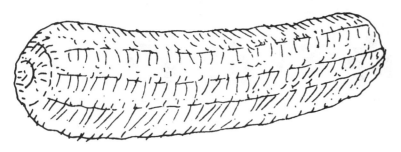

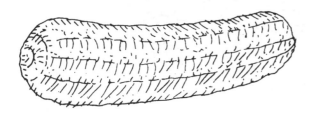

_____

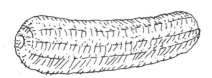

_____

_____

Skills: Measuring length; Counting; Writing numerals

BASIC MATH SKILLS

Will the dolls fit in my doll bed?
Use the ruler to find out the length of each doll.
Look at the doll in each box.
Count the numbers to show how long it is.
Then write the numeral on the line.

_____   _____   _____

Skills: Measuring length; Counting; Writing numerals

PRACTICE PAGE

PRACTICE PAGE

TIME AND MONEY

Look at the pictures in each box.
Circle the picture of the activity
that takes more time to do.

Skills: Time awareness; Identifying which takes more time

TIME AND MONEY

Look at the pictures in each box.
Circle the picture of the activity
that takes less time to do.

Skills: Time awareness; Identifying which takes less time

TIME AND MONEY

What time is it?
Look at each clock.
Write the time.

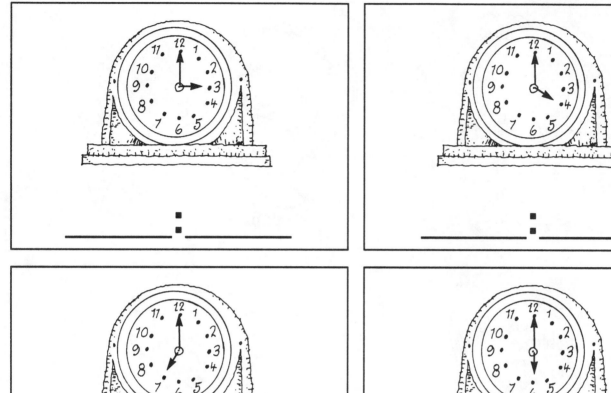

_____ **:** _____

_____ **:** _____

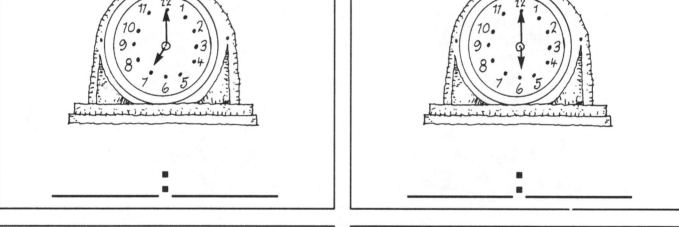

_____ **:** _____

_____ **:** _____

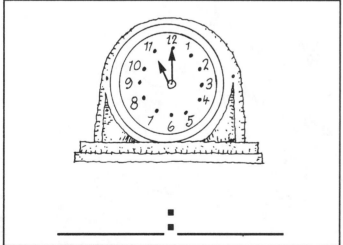

_____ **:** _____

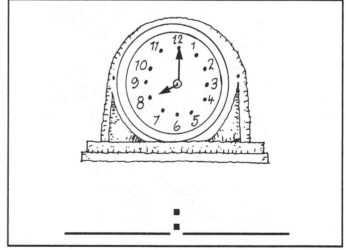

_____ **:** _____

Skills: Time awareness; Telling time to the hour

TIME AND MONEY

Tell me the time.
Look at each clock.
Write the time.

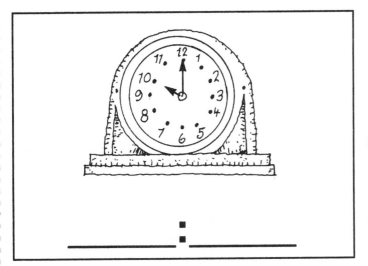

_____ : _____

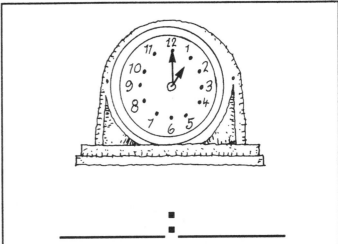

_____ : _____

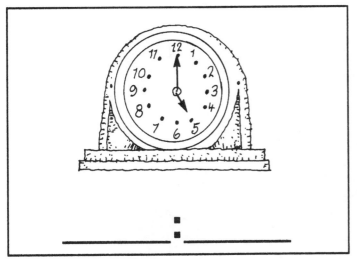

_____ : _____

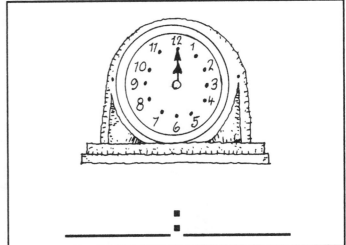

_____ : _____

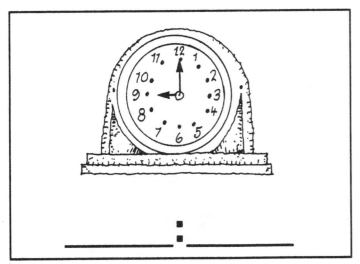

_____ : _____

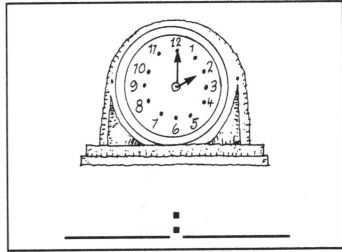

_____ : _____

Skills: Time awareness; Telling time to the hour

TIME AND MONEY

Put the time on the clock!
Look at the time.
Draw the hands on each clock to show the correct time.

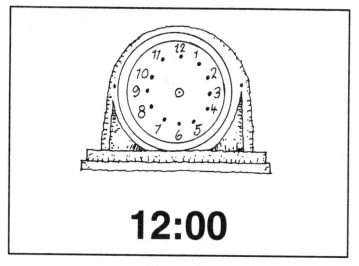

12:00

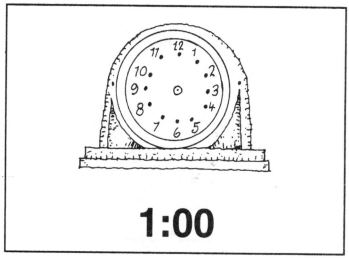

1:00

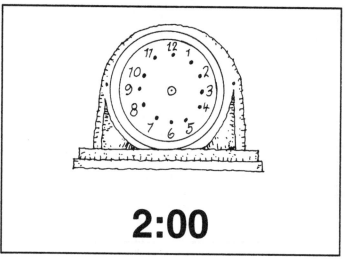

2:00

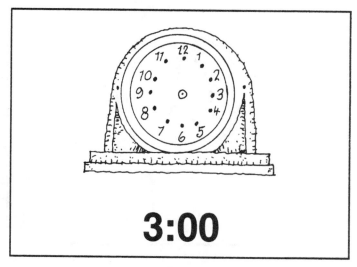

3:00

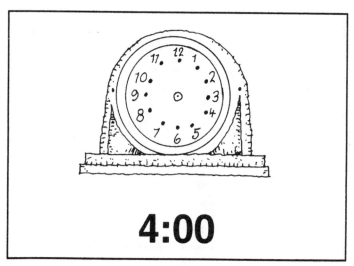

4:00

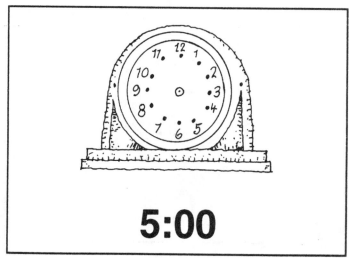

5:00

Skills: Time awareness; Showing time to the hour

TIME AND MONEY

Can I buy it?
A nickel is worth five cents.
A nickel is the same as five pennies.
Put an **X** on the coins you need to buy each toy.

6¢

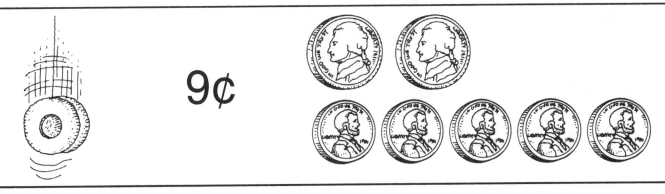

8¢

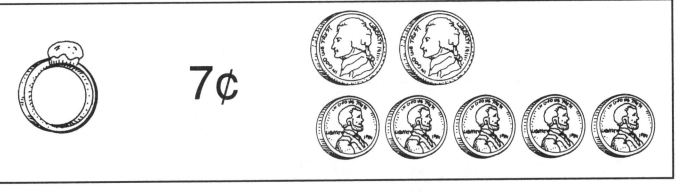

7¢

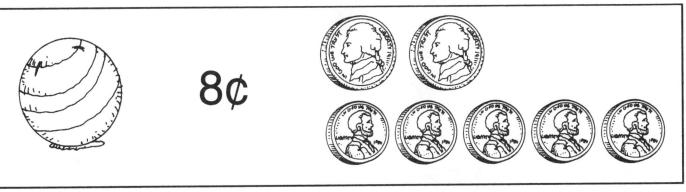

9¢

Skills: Money awareness; Understanding the value of a penny and a nickel

TIME AND MONEY

Can I buy it?

A dime is worth 10 cents.

A dime is the same as 10 pennies or 2 nickels.

Put an **X** on the coins you need to buy each toy.

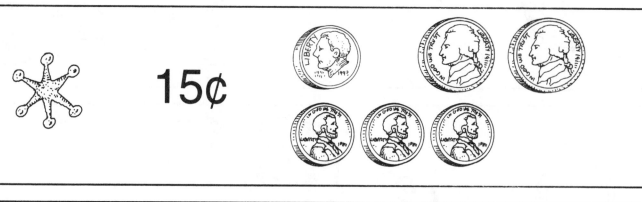

Skills: Money awareness; Understanding the value of a penny, a nickel, and a dime

TIME AND MONEY

How much does it cost?
How much money is needed to buy each item?
Draw a line to show the the money that matches each price tag.

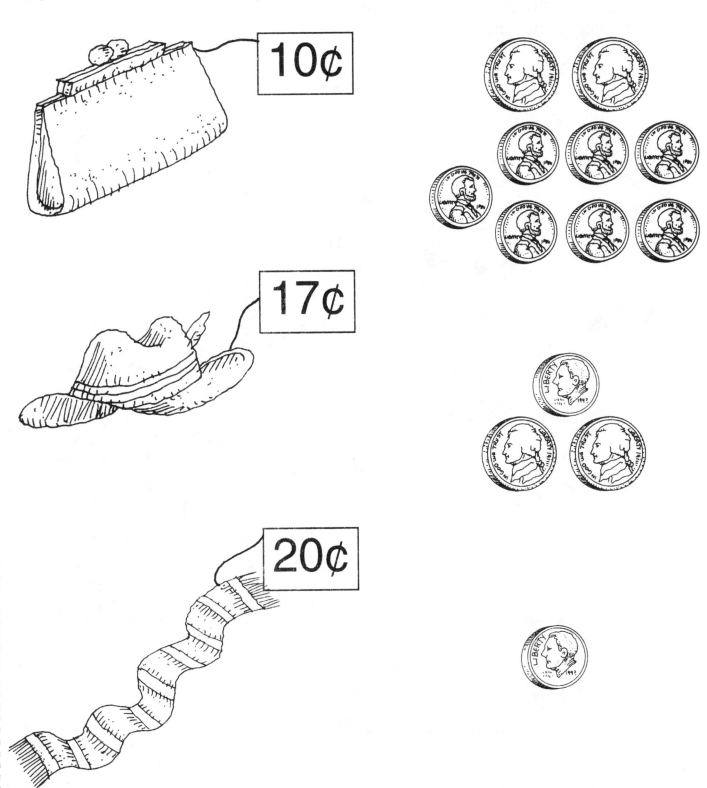

10¢

17¢

20¢

READING READINESS

Look at the cookies we baked!
Look at the letter in each cookie.
Color the cookies with lowercase letters one color.
Color the cookies with uppercase letters another color.
Then finish coloring the picture.

Skills: Distinguishing upper and lowercase letters; Recognizing letters; Developing fine motor skills

READING READINESS

Look at each picture.
Draw lines between the things that are the same.

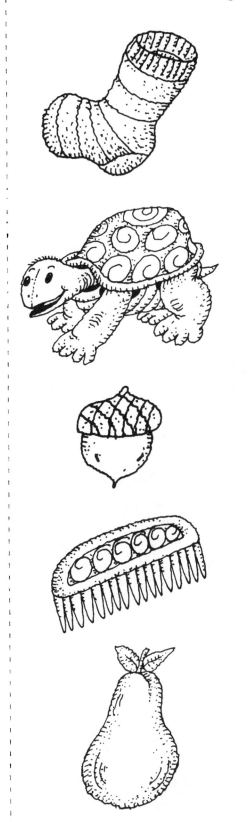

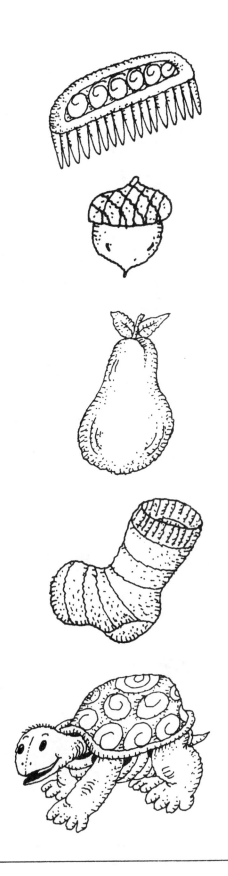

Skills: Visual matching; Classification

READING READINESS

Color the two pictures in each box that go together.

Skills: Association; Classification; Logical reasoning

READING READINESS

Look at the pictures in each row.
Cross out the one that is different.

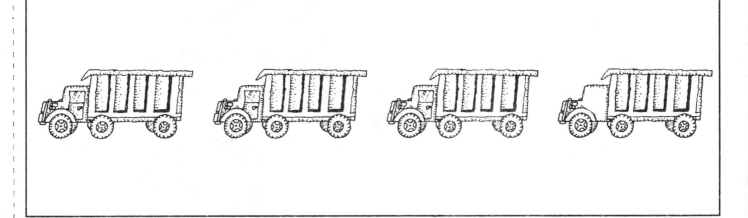

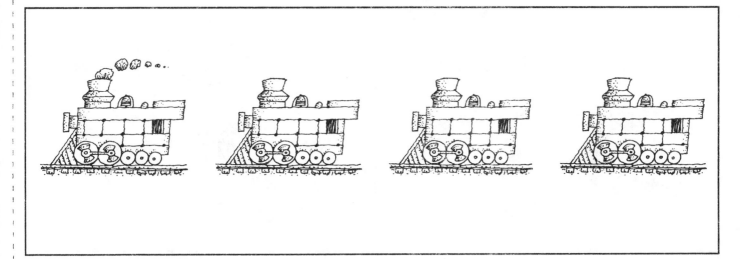

Skills: Visual discrimination; Noticing details

READING READINESS

Which one does not belong?
Cross out the one that does not belong with the others.
Then color the other pictures.

Skills: Classification; Association

READING READINESS

Look closely at each row of pictures.
One of the objects is in a different position.
Cross it out and then color the other pictures.

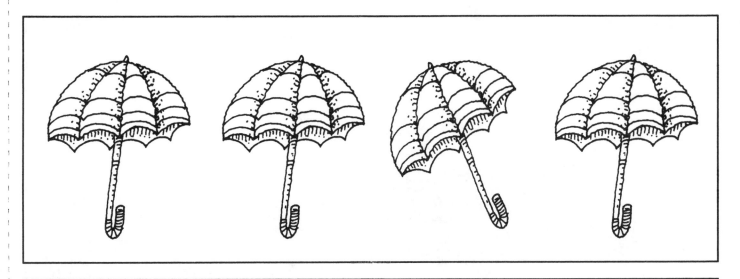

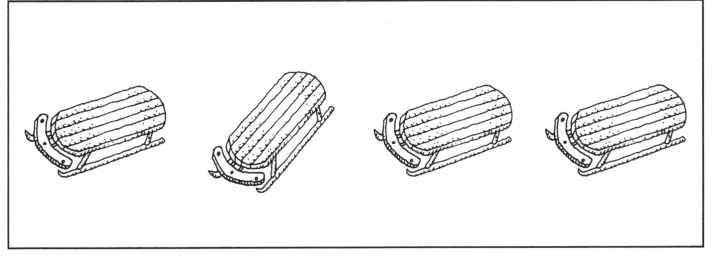

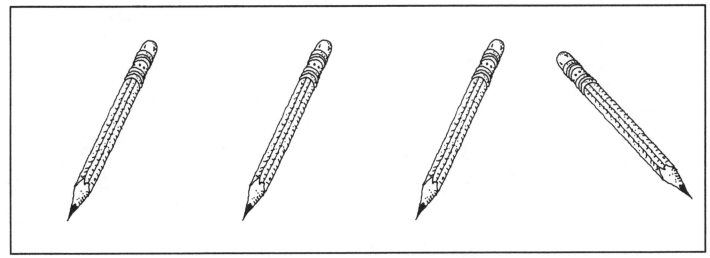

Skills: Visual discrimination; Noticing details; Spatial orientation

READING READINESS

Look at the large pictures.
Then look at the detail in each small box.

Find the detail in each large picture and circle it.
Then color the pictures.

Skills: Visual discrimination; Noticing details

READING READINESS

Look at the pictures in each box.
Circle the pictures that are facing right.
Make an "X" over the pictures that are facing left.

Skills: Recognizing right and left

READING READINESS

Look at the first picture in each row and say its name.
Circle the picture whose name rhymes with it.

Skills: Auditory discrimination; Reproducing sounds

READING READINESS

Look at each picture.
Draw a line between each pair of pictures whose names rhyme.

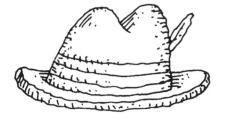
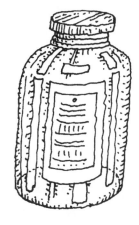
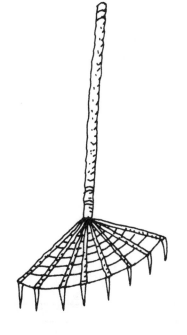

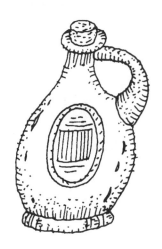

Skills: Auditory discrimination; Reproducing sounds

READING READINESS

Look at the pattern in each row.
Draw a line to the picture that continues each pattern.

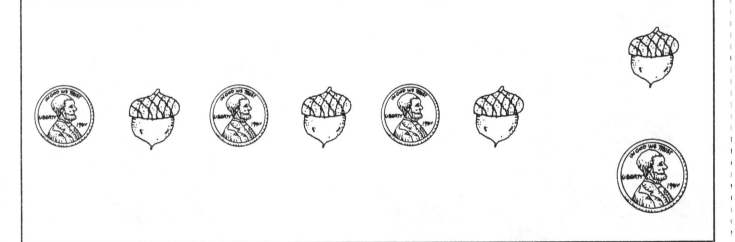

Skills: Observing and continuing patterns; Visual memory

READING READINESS

Look at the pattern in each row.
Draw a line to the picture that continues each pattern.

Skills: Observing and continuing patterns; Visual memory

READING READINESS

Look at the puppies.
Which ones are the same?
Draw lines to connect the ones that are alike.

Skills: Matching; Recognizing similarities

READING READINESS

The princess lost her slipper.
Help her find it.
Look at the slippers on this page.
Draw lines to connect the ones that are alike.
The one that does not have a match belongs to the princess.
Circle the princess's missing slipper.

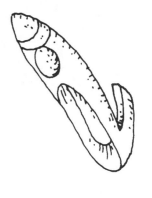

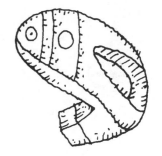

Skills: Matching; Recognizing similarities

READING READINESS

The animals are heading back to the zoo.
Draw a line to connect each animal with its shadow.

Skills: Matching; Recognizing similarities

READING READINESS

Draw a line to connect each vehicle with its shadow.

Skills: Matching; Recognizing similarities

READING READINESS

Look at the picture at the beginning of each row.
Then look at the other pictures in that row.
One picture is the same as the first one, but turned another way.
Find and circle that picture.

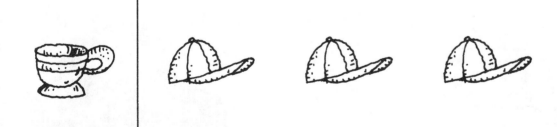

Skills: Noticing details; Recognizing differences

READING READINESS

Look at the picture at the beginning of each row.
Then look at the other pictures in that row.
One picture is the same as the first one, but turned another way.
Find and circle that picture.

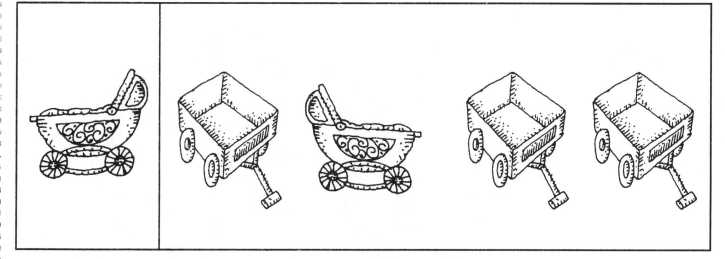

Skills: Noticing details; Recognizing differences

READING READINESS

Look at the girl's ring.
Then look at the stones below.
Circle the one that is exactly like the stone in the girl's ring.

    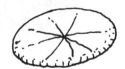

Skills: Noticing details; Recognizing differences

READING READINESS

Let's play dress-up.
Look at the girls on this page.
Find and circle the one that looks different.
Then color the rest of the pictures.

Skills: Noticing details; Recognizing differences

READING READINESS

Work the puzzle!
Look at the finished puzzle.
Look at the loose pieces.
Draw lines to connect each puzzle piece to its match in the completed puzzle.

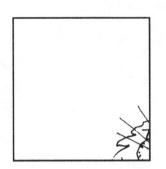

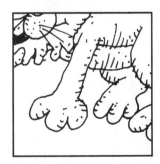

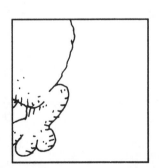

Skills: Spatial awareness; Visual perception; Developing fine motor skills

READING READINESS

Look at the finished puzzle.
Look at the loose pieces.
Draw lines to connect each puzzle piece to its match in the completed puzzle.

 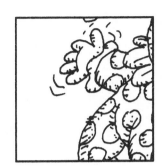 

Skills: Spatial awareness; Visual perception; Developing fine motor skills

READING READINESS

Look at the picture.
Then look at the puzzle pieces.
Number the pieces, in order, from top to bottom.

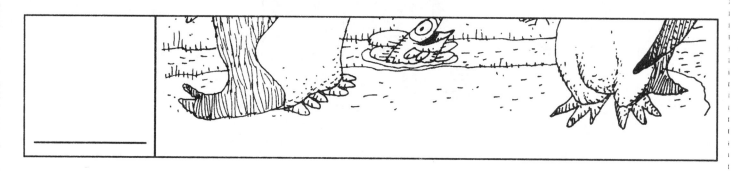

Skills: Spatial awareness; Visual perception; Developing fine motor skills

READING READINESS

Look at the monkey.
Then look at the puzzle pieces.
Number the pieces, in order, from top to bottom.

Skills: Spatial awareness; Visual perception; Developing fine motor skills

READING READINESS

Let's climb and jump and slide!
Look at the detail in each small box.
Find that detail in the picture below and circle it.

1

2

3

Skills: Noticing details

READING READINESS

The ship is ready to sail.
But some strange things have been stored on board.
Look at each object in the box.
Then find and circle each one in the picture below.

Skills: Visual perception; Visual memory

READING READINESS

School is fun.
But there are things that do not belong in the classroom.
Find and circle each.

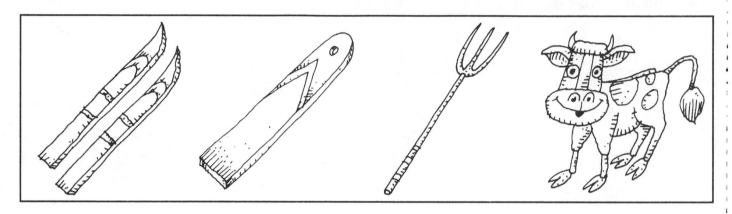

Skills: Thinking logically; Visual perception; Visual memory

READING READINESS

Dancing is such fun!
Look closely at both pictures.
Then circle five things that are at the top of the page
that are missing from the picture at the bottom.

Skills: Noticing details; Recognizing differences; Visual memory

READING READINESS

Let's color and paint today!
Look at both pictures.
Then circle five things at the top of the page that
are missing from the picture at the bottom.

Skills: Noticing details; Recognizing differences; Visual memory

READING READINESS

Sailing, sailing...
Look at both pictures.
Then circle five things at the top of the page that
are missing from the picture at the bottom.

Skills: Noticing details; Recognizing differences; Visual memory

READING READINESS

Mother and Father are getting ready for a party,
but some things are very wrong.
Circle all the things that are wrong in the picture.

Skills: Noticing details; Recognizing differences; Thinking logically

READING READINESS

What are the detectives looking for?
Find and circle the hidden letters.
Write each letter on the dashed lines below.
Then unscramble the letters to see what the detectives are looking for.

_____ _____ _____ _____ _____

Skills: Recognizing letters; Vocabulary

READING READINESS

What are the children building?
Find and circle the hidden letters.
Write each letter on the dashed lines below.
Then unscramble the letters to see what the children are building.

___   ___   ___   ___   ___   ___

Skills: Recognizing letters; Vocabulary

READING READINESS

Toys, toys are everywhere!
Look carefully at all the toys.
When you are ready, turn the page to play a memory game.

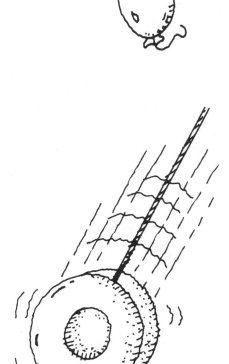

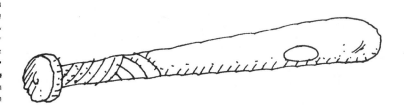

Skills: Visual memory; Association; Thinking logically

READING READINESS

Look at the pictures on this page.
Which ones do you remember from page 175?
Circle the ones you remember.

Skills: Visual memory; Association; Thinking logically

READING READINESS

Look at the sets of objects on the left.
Then find an object on the right that belongs to each set.
Draw lines to connect them.

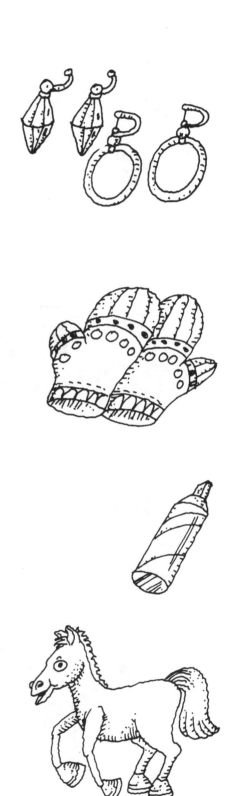

READING READINESS

Draw lines to connect each wheel to its vehicle.

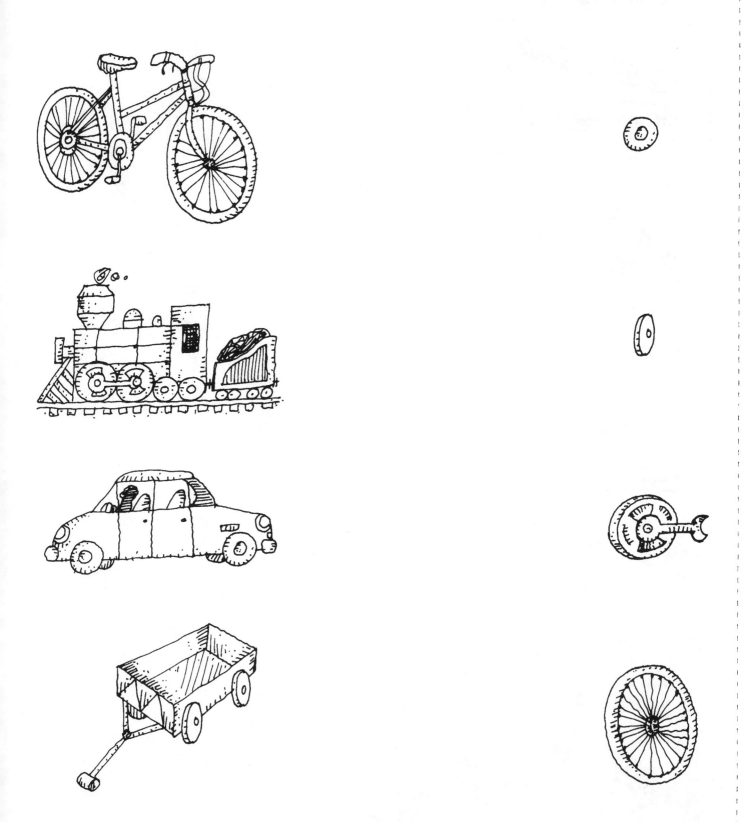

Skills: Classifying; Thinking logically; Visual matching

READING READINESS

Home, sweet home!
Look at each object at the top of the page.
Look at each room of the house.
Decide where each object belongs.
Then write its number in the correct box below.

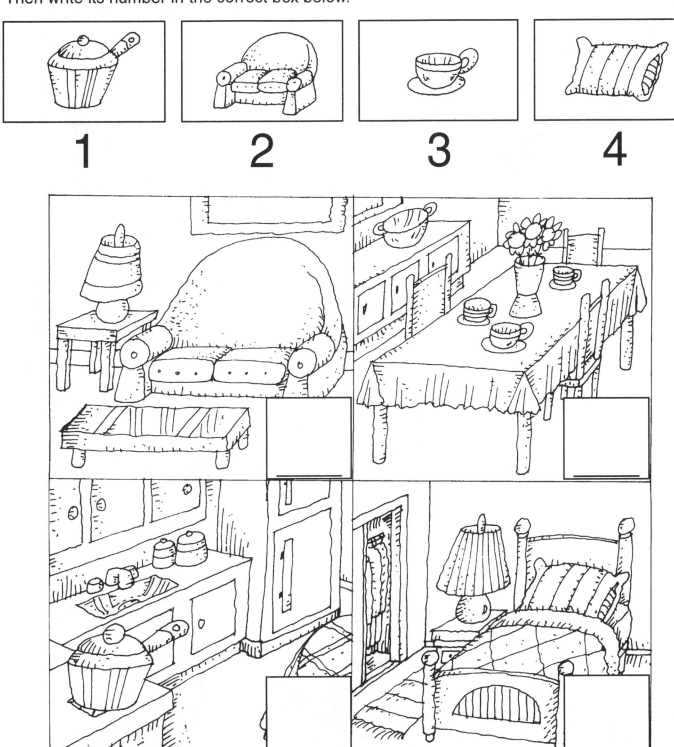

1   2   3   4

Skills: Thinking logically; Developing fine motor skills

READING READINESS

We need to sort the laundry!
Look at the clothes and the baskets below.
Draw lines to sort the clothes into the correct baskets.

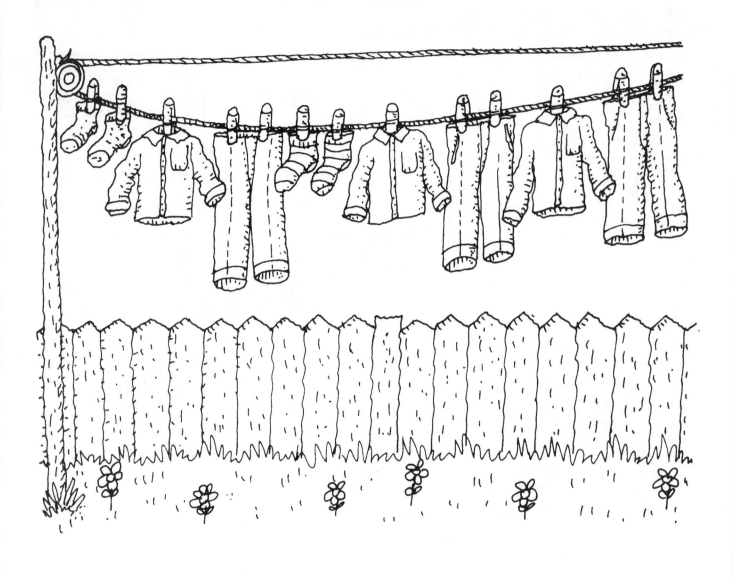

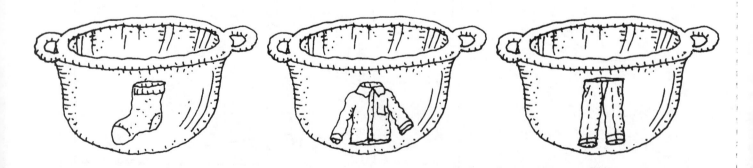

Skills: Classifying; Thinking logically

READING READINESS

Which things are alive?
Look at the pictures on this page.
Circle all the living things.
Put a line under all the things that are not alive.

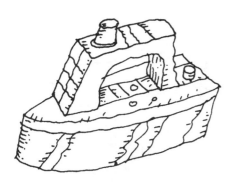

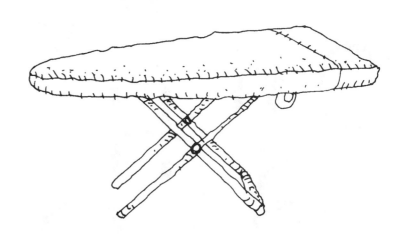

Skills: Classifying; Thinking logically

READING READINESS

Put the lowercase letters in the top box.
Put the uppercase letters in the bottom box.
Draw lines to connect each letter to its right box.

e j a H

p m k

D n H

B Q

f A

P f i e

letters

LETTERS

Skills: Classifying; Thinking logically; Recognizing upper and lowercase letters

READING READINESS

Let's collect shells!
Look at the shells and the piles below.
Draw lines to sort them into the correct piles.

Skills: Classifying; Thinking logically; Sorting

READING READINESS

The train needs to get down the mountain.
Follow the path that leads to the station.

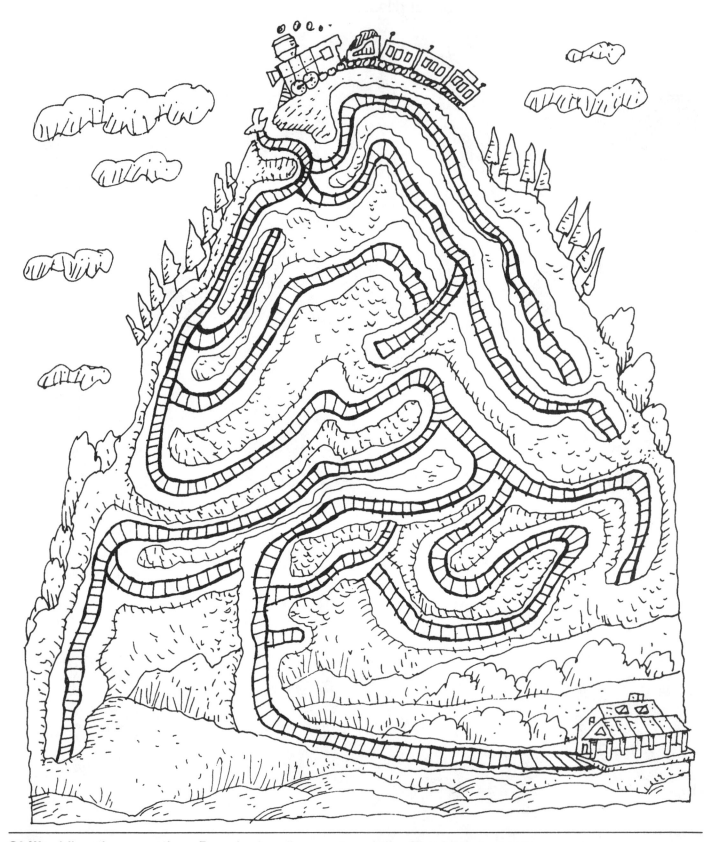

Skills: Visual perception; Developing fine motor skills; Thinking logically

READING READINESS

Here comes the balloon!
Follow the path through the clouds to the landing site.

Skills: Visual perception; Developing fine motor skills; Thinking logically

READING READINESS

Trace the lines to see who is flying each kite.

Skills: Visual perception; Thinking logically; Developing fine motor skills; Eye/hand coordination

READING READINESS

The squirrels are looking for nuts.
Each squirrel will find a nut.
Follow each path to see what each squirrel finds.

Skills: Visual perception; Thinking logically; Developing fine motor skills; Eye/hand coordination

READING READINESS

It's time for the animals to sleep.
Follow the path from each animal.
Trace the lines to show where each animal goes to sleep.

Skills: Visual perception; Thinking logically; Developing fine motor skills; Eye/hand coordination

READING READINESS

What a cute doll!
Finish the picture of the doll so that both sides will
match exactly if it is folded on the dashed line.

Skills: Developing fine motor skills; Eye/hand coordination; Thinking logically

READING READINESS

Finish the picture of the butterfly so that both sides will
match exactly if it is folded on the dashed line.

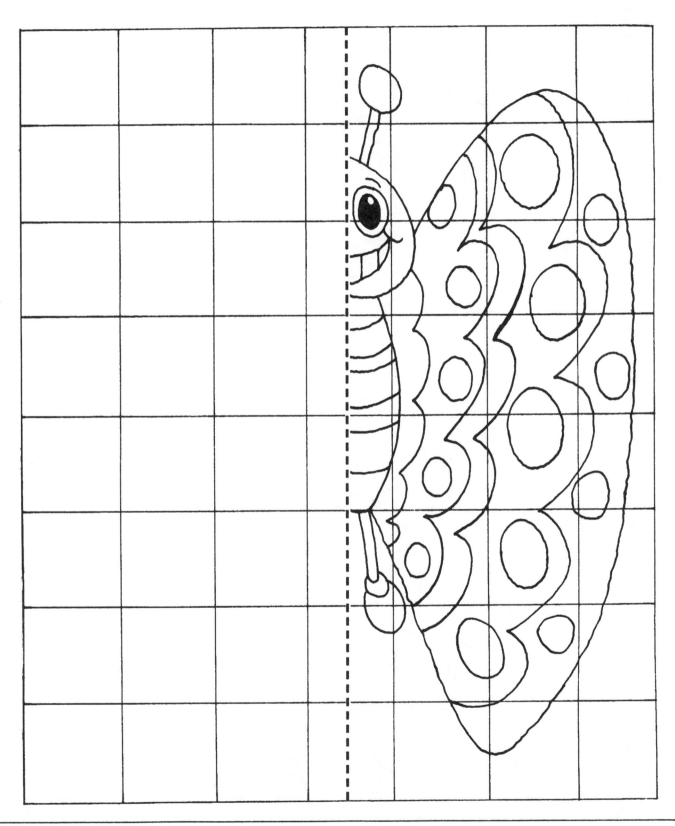

Skills: Developing fine motor skills; Eye/hand coordination; Thinking logically

READING READINESS

What is it?
Look at the unfinished picture.
Think about what it might be.
Complete the picture to show what you think it is.

Skills: Thinking logically; Developing fine motor skills; Problem solving

READING READINESS

What will happen **next**?
Look at the scene on the left in each row.
Look at the two pictures on the right.
Circle the picture that shows what will happen next.
Then tell a story about the picture.

Skills: Sequencing; Predicting; Thinking logically

192

READING READINESS

What happens **before**?
Look at the picture on the left in each row.
Look at the two pictures on the right.
Circle the picture that shows what will happen before.

Skills: Sequencing; Predicting; Thinking logically

READING READINESS

What happens next?
Look at the pictures at the top of the page.
Tell a story about the pictures.
Then draw a picture to show what happens next.

Skills: Sequencing; Thinking logically; Developing fine motor skills; Understanding story order

READING READINESS

What happens first? next? last?
The pictures in each row tell a story, but they are mixed up.
Write the numbers 1, 2, and 3 in the boxes to put the story in order.
Then tell the story.

Skills: Sequencing; Thinking logically; Understanding story order

READING READINESS

These pictures tell a story, but the pictures are mixed up.
Write the numbers 1, 2, 3, and 4 in the boxes to put the story in order.
Then tell the story.

Skills: Sequencing; Thinking logically; Understanding story order

READING READINESS

Think about your day.
Look at the pictures on this page.
Circle the pictures that show things you use in the winter.
Underline the pictures that show things you use in summer.

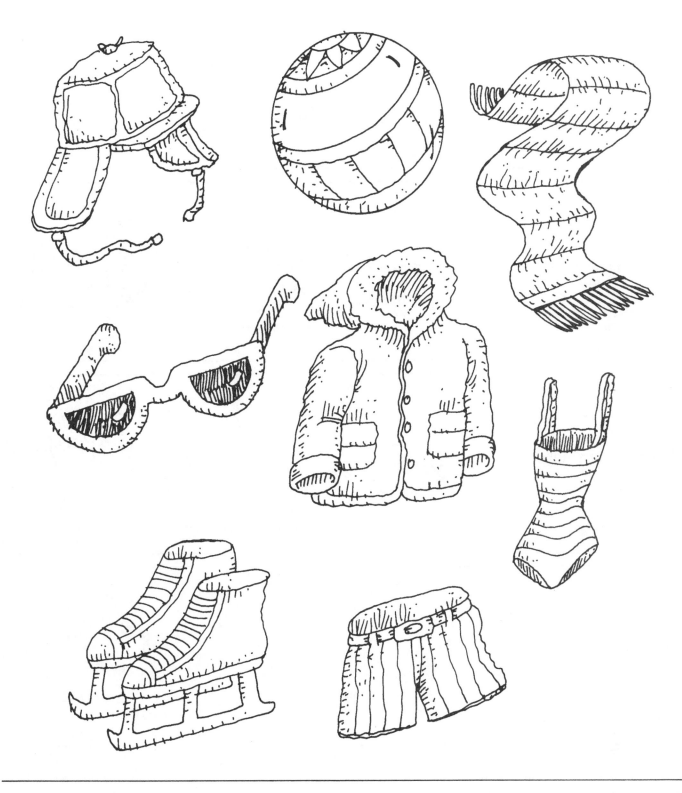

Skills: Thinking logically; Classifying

READING READINESS

Listen to the questions.
Circle your answers.

Which goes fastest?

Which is slowest?

Which is the smallest?

Which is the tallest?

Skills: Thinking logically; Problem solving

READING READINESS

Yummy!
Draw lines to connect each food on the right to
something that it is made of on the left.

Skills: Associating; Problem solving; Thinking logically

READING READINESS

Who is the real princess?
The real princess has bows in her hair and a rose on her dress.
Circle the real princess.

Skills: Deductive reasoning; Problem solving; Logical reasoning; Visual discrimination

PHONICS RIDDLE BOOK

About the Phonics and Language in This Book

The riddles in this section are designed to help children focus on initial consonants. As you read, point out the letters at the top of the page and discuss the sound they make. Then read each riddle and discuss the job it describes. Help the child recognize the connection between the sound of the job name and the letter on that page. To reinforce this, you can make a list of the letters that the child recognizes. Then write as many words that begin with that sound as the child can name. Seeing words in print will help to reinforce a child's understanding of sounds and symbols.

Once your child has mastered the initial consonants, you can teach other challenging phonics concepts with this book. Look in the box at the bottom of each page to see which ones are emphasized. On the reverse of the page, you will find a list of words illustrating the highlighted concepts. For instance, some pages highlight long vowels. You can invite your child to find all the long vowel words on that page. Or point out a word with a specific long vowel, and invite the child to find a word with a sound that matches.

The use of rhyme in this book helps emerging readers to predict words and follow the rhythm of each sentence. Encourage the child to fill in a rhyming word or guess what the last word in a sentence might be. Making predictions such as these helps a child to build confidence and identify new words.

The element of repetition in this book also encourages beginning readers to follow the pattern of the language and predict words. Help the child notice how some sentences have similar words in them.

People At Work

What do people do all day?
Do they work? Do they play?
Look around you, and you'll see
People busy as can be,
Working through the day or night
To try to get the job done right.

Here's a set of riddles
About things people do.
Read what happens in each job,
Then try to guess just who
Would do each one, and use
The starting letter as a clue.

Our jobs start with S. One of us works inside.
The other moves around a lot, and changes with the tide.

I answer phones, take messages and type from nine to five.
I make appointments, and I help to make your business thrive.
Who am I?

I swab the deck while singing on my sailboat out at sea.
On the salty ocean water, I feel so nice and free!
Who am I?

Ss

secretary

sailor

Can you draw something that begins with the sound that S makes?

Our jobs fit us to a T.
Try to guess who we can be!

T t

I hem and stitch, I tuck and trim
To make your clothing fit.
If it's too tight, just call on me,
And I'll take care of it.
Who am I?

With a racket and a fuzzy ball,
I run around the court.
I love to win, but if I don't,
I'll still be a good sport.
Who am I?

short vowels ă, ĭ, ŭ

tailor

tennis player

T t

Can you draw something that begins with the sound that T makes?

What jobs begin with letter B?
Read the clues, and you will see.

I make cookies, bread, and cakes.
When it comes to pastry, I've got what it takes.
Who am I?

In my pink tutu I strike a pose
As I dance for you on my tippy-toes.
Who am I?

long vowels ā, ē, ō, ū

baker

Bb

ballerina

Can you draw something that begins with the sound that B makes?

Long a
make
cakes
takes

Long e
read
see

Long o
pose
toes

Long u
clues
tutu

Hear the sound that starts each job's name!
That H sound is our claim to fame!

Hh

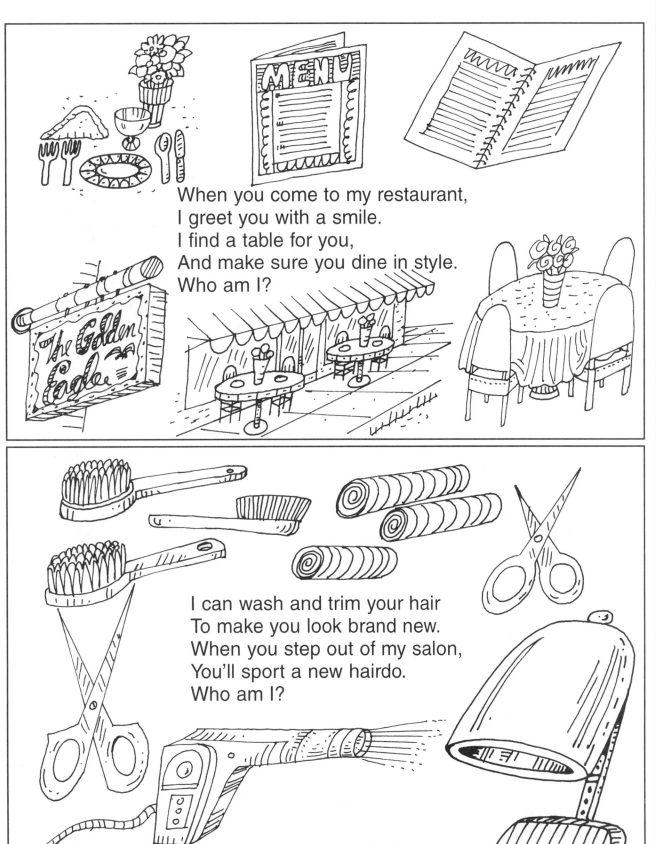

When you come to my restaurant,
I greet you with a smile.
I find a table for you,
And make sure you dine in style.
Who am I?

I can wash and trim your hair
To make you look brand new.
When you step out of my salon,
You'll sport a new hairdo.
Who am I?

hostess

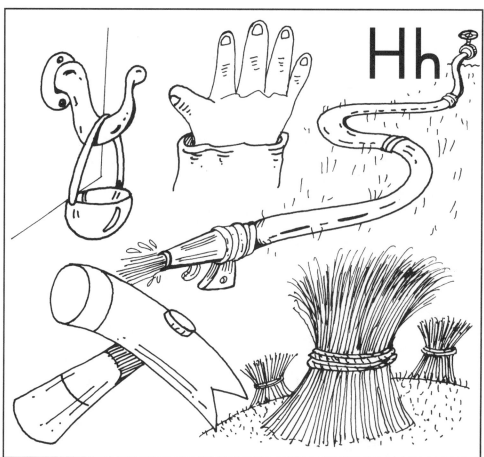

Hh

hairstylist

Can you draw something that begins with the sound that H makes?

Many jobs begin with M.
Here are clues to two of them.

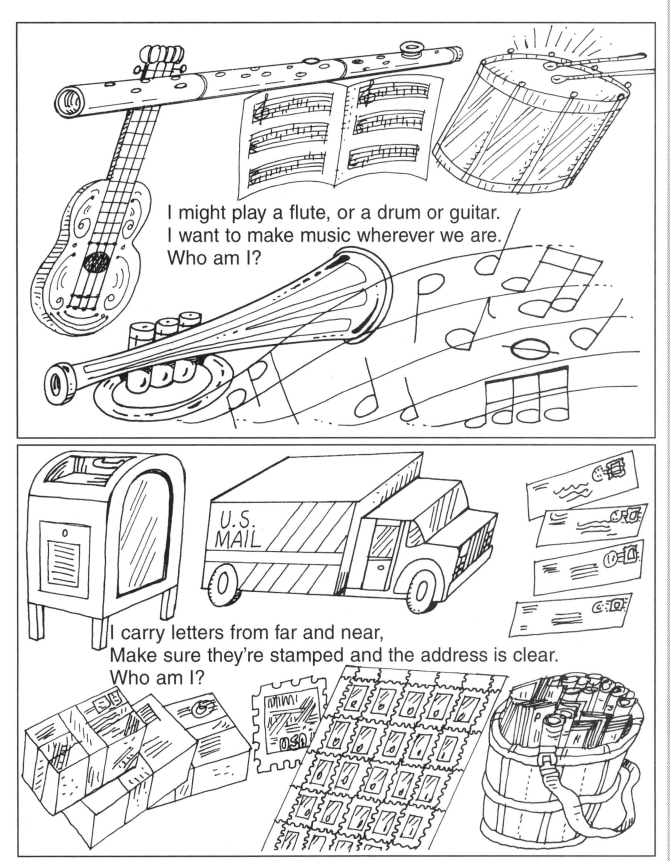

I might play a flute, or a drum or guitar.
I want to make music wherever we are.
Who am I?

U.S. MAIL

I carry letters from far and near,
Make sure they're stamped and the address is clear.
Who am I?

musician

Mm

mail carrier

Can you draw something that begins with the sound that M makes?

J stands for jobs, some work and some play.
Here's one of each; both start with J.

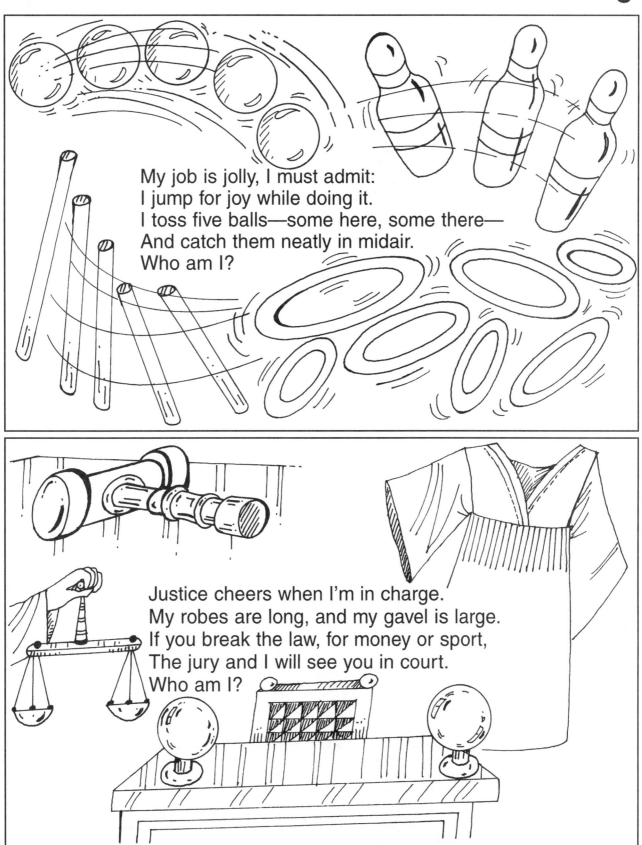

My job is jolly, I must admit:
I jump for joy while doing it.
I toss five balls—some here, some there—
And catch them neatly in midair.
Who am I?

Justice cheers when I'm in charge.
My robes are long, and my gavel is large.
If you break the law, for money or sport,
The jury and I will see you in court.
Who am I?

juggler

J j

judge

Can you draw something that begins with the sound that J makes?

Jobs that start with F are found
In city and country. Just look around.

I plough the fields and feed each duck,
While the fussy hens call, "Cluck, cluck, cluck."
Who am I?

In my fine red truck with its flashing light,
I fight fires both day and night.
Who am I?

farmer

fire fighter

Ff

Can you draw something that begins with the sound that F makes?

We work outdoors the whole year 'round.
Our jobs both start with the hard G sound.

The truck goes first. I run behind
And gather trash for it to grind.
Who am I?

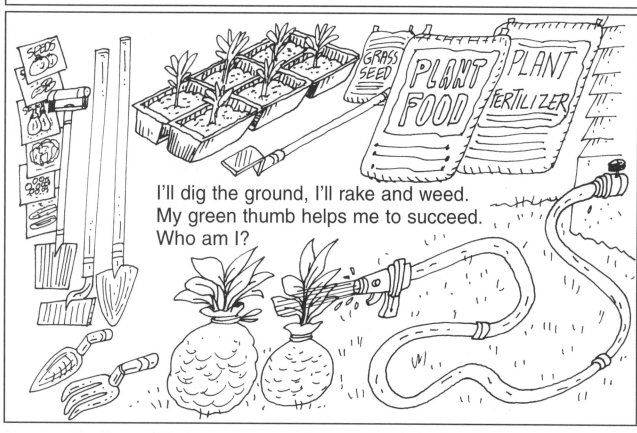

I'll dig the ground, I'll rake and weed.
My green thumb helps me to succeed.
Who am I?

final consonant blend: nd

Gg

garbage collector

gardener

Can you draw something that begins with the sound that G makes?

Our jobs begin with the sound of D.
What do we do? Turn the page to see.

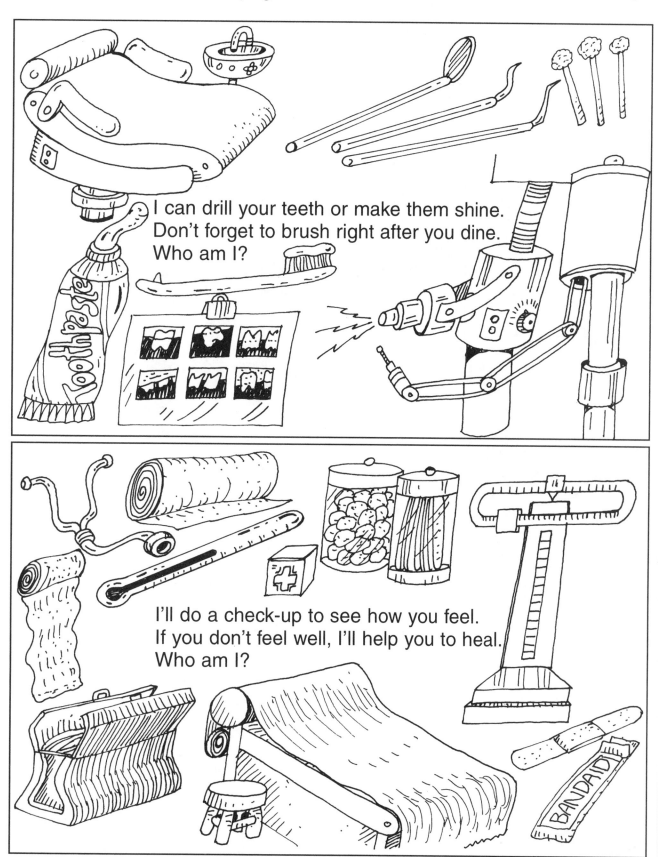

I can drill your teeth or make them shine.
Don't forget to brush right after you dine.
Who am I?

I'll do a check-up to see how you feel.
If you don't feel well, I'll help you to heal.
Who am I?

Dd

dentist

doctor

Can you draw something that begins with the sound that D makes?

Long a	Long e	Long i
page	we	I
make	see	shine
	teeth	right
	feel	dine
	heal	

Listen for L; it's the letter you'll hear.
Then look at the clues, and the answers are clear.

I can fix your locks, so they'll open and close,
Or make lovely new keys, as everyone knows.
Who am I?

I can help you check out good things to read.
I like to lend people the books that they need.
Who am I?

short/long vowel ĕ/ē

locksmith

LI

librarian

Can you draw something that begins with the sound that L makes?

Short e words
letter
then
help
check
lend

Long e words
keys
read
people
need

The next jobs start with the sound of N.
Now it's time to guess again.

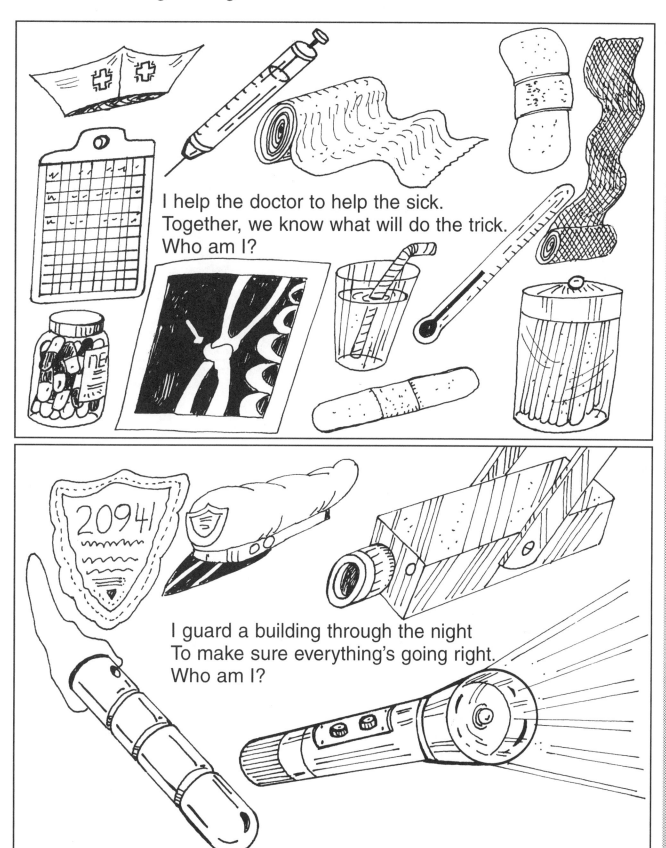

I help the doctor to help the sick.
Together, we know what will do the trick.
Who am I?

I guard a building through the night
To make sure everything's going right.
Who am I?

Nn

nurse

night watchman

Can you draw something that begins with the sound that N makes?

If you think of the hard sound a C can make,
Guessing our jobs is a piece of cake.

Cc

With a hammer and nails I can build anything.
I make cabinets and tables, even a swing!
Who am I?

I make good things for you to eat:
My tasty meals just can't be beat.
Who am I?

long/short vowel ā/ă

carpenter

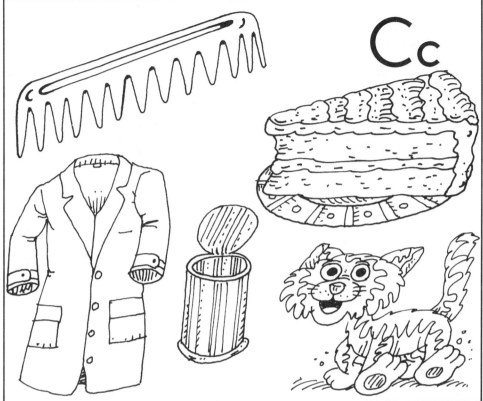

C c

cook

Can you draw something that begins with the sound that C makes?

Long a	Short a
make	can
cake	hammer
nails	cabinets
tables	and
tasty	am

In these careers you can go far.
Just remember to start with R.

To cover my beat, I rise at dawn,
I take note of what's going on.
My story tells you here and now,
Who, what, where, when, why and how!
Who am I?

My rhythm is rock, my songs are loud;
My concerts really attract a crowd.
When I'm on stage, the rafters shake.
I guarantee you'll stay awake!
Who am I?

consonant digraph: wh

reporter

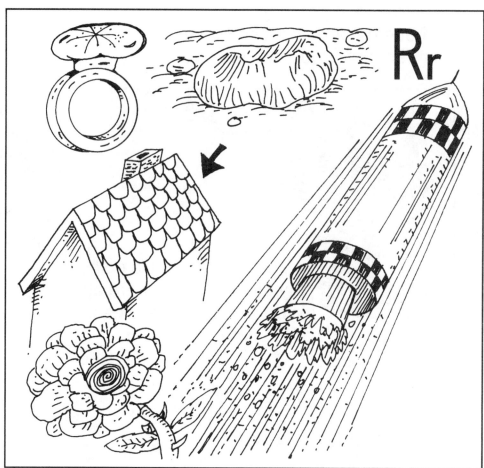

R r

rock star

Can you draw something that begins with the sound that R makes?

Follow the clues and you will see interesting careers that begin with P.

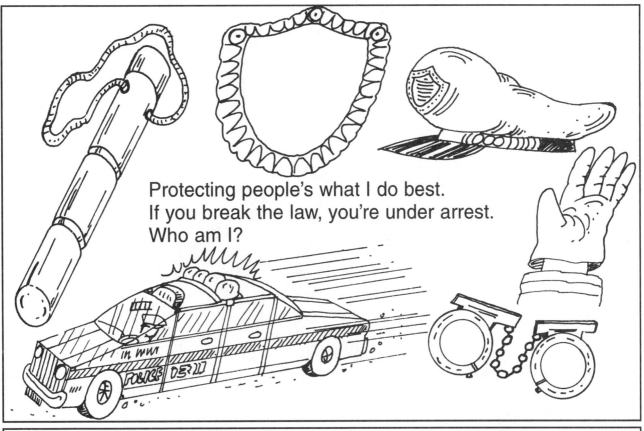

Protecting people's what I do best.
If you break the law, you're under arrest.
Who am I?

I bring my passengers way up high.
My plane flies fleetly through the sky.
Who am I?

consonant blends: pr, br, pl, fl, sk

Pp

police officer

pilot

Can you draw something that begins with the sound that P makes?

You've practiced each sound, you've used each clue,
You've solved each riddle—good for you!
Now out of these jobs, both old and new,
Which ones would you like to do?

_____

- -

_____

_____

- -

_____

_____

- -

_____

_____

- -

_____

Write the names of your favorite jobs on the lines.
Then draw a picture of your favorite one.

Here are some phonics and language ideas to try:

Make a double set of flash cards using the letters from the riddles. Lay the cards in rows face down on a table. Play concentration with the child. Each player turns over a pair of cards. Players try to name the letters and say a word that begins with each letter. Players keep the cards that match if they can name the letter and say a word that begins with that sound. The player with the most cards wins.

Encourage the child to think of other jobs that begin with each letter. If the child can't think of a job, a word will do.

Have the child draw a picture to go with each letter in the book. Make the pictures into a small sounds and letters book.

Help the child find words that are easy to rhyme and make word families. Choose a word like *sick.* Encourage the child to make a list of words that rhyme with sick such as kick, pick, stick, lick, tick and so on.

PHONICS SKILLS I

Look at the pictures and the letters that make their ending sounds.
Look at the pictures and the letters at the bottom of the page.
Draw a line from each picture to the letter that makes its ending sound.

g   p   t

PHONICS SKILLS I

Look at the pictures and the letters that make their ending sounds.
Then look at the pictures and letters at the bottom of the page.
Draw a line from each picture to the letter that makes its ending sound.

Skills: Developing auditory discrimination; Matching ending sounds; Recognizing letter/sound relationships

PHONICS SKILLS I

Look at the letter on each easel.
Look at the pictures on each easel.
Circle the picture whose name begins
with the sound that the letter makes.

Skills: Developing auditory discrimination; Matching beginning sounds; Recognizing
letter/sound relationships

PHONICS SKILLS I

Play this letter game.

Take turns tossing a penny or counter onto the house.

Name the letter that the penny falls on and a word that begins with that letter.

Collect one point for every correct answer.

The first person to reach 10 points wins.

Skills: Recognizing letter/sound relationships; Developing words for sounds

PHONICS SKILLS I

Look at the pictures and the letters that make their ending sounds.
Then look at the pictures and letters at the bottom of the page.
Draw a line from each picture to the letter that makes its ending sound.

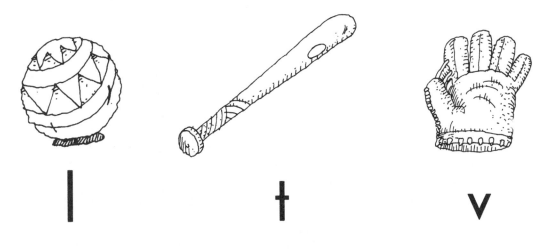

l   t   v

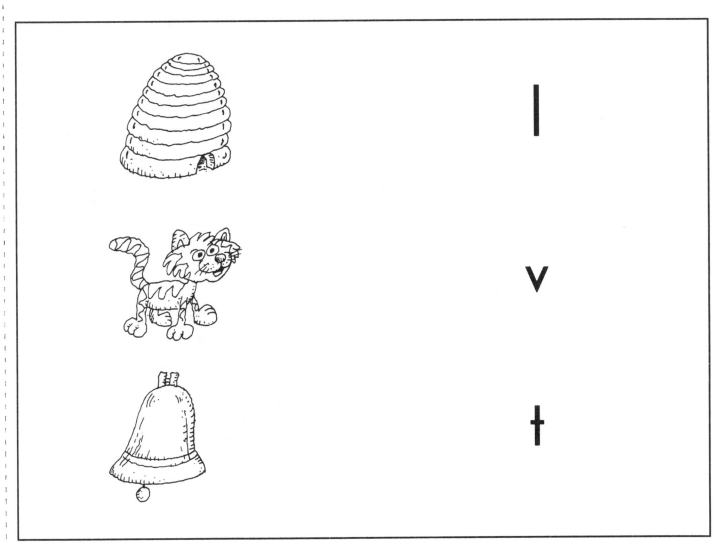

Skills: Developing auditory discrimination; Matching ending sounds; Recognizing letter/sound relationships

PHONICS SKILLS I

The balloon is trying to land.
Follow the path of vowels, **a, e, i, o, u,**
through the maze to the field.

Skills: Recognizing letters as vowels; Using visual perception skills; Developing fine motor skills

PHONICS SKILLS I

The family is going camping.
Follow the path of vowels, **a**, **e**, **i**, **o**, **u**,
through the maze to help them get to the campsite.

Skills: Recognizing letters as vowels; Using visual perception skills; Developing fine motor skills

PHONICS SKILLS I

Look at the pictures on this set of blocks.
Sock has a short **o** sound. **Coat** has a long **o** sound.
Circle the pictures whose names have the short **o** sound.
Underline the pictures whose names have the long **o** sound.

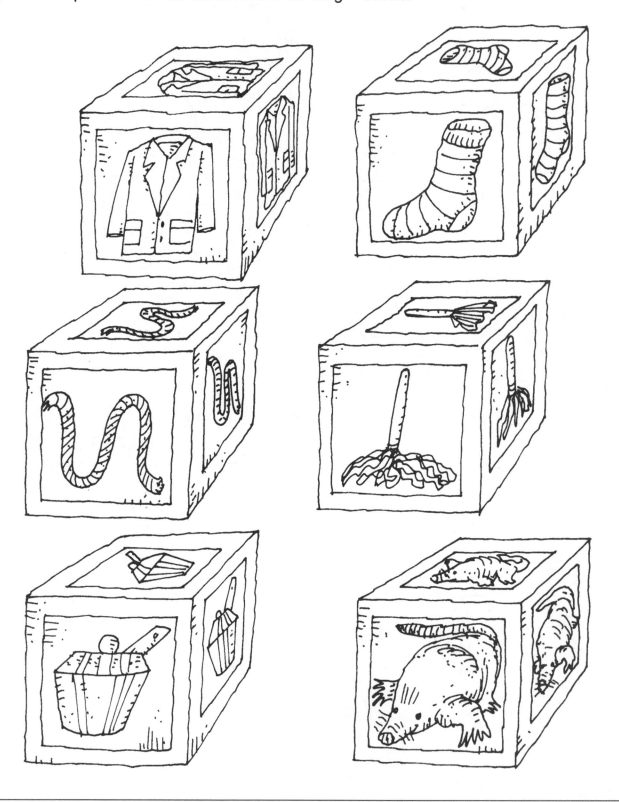

Skills: Using auditory discrimination skills; Understanding sound/symbol association;
Differentiating short and long vowel sounds

PHONICS SKILLS I

Let's have a party.
Put on a **hat**. Have some **cake**.
Hat has a short **a** sound. **Cake** has a long **a** sound.
Look at the pictures on this page.
Circle the pictures whose names have the short **a** sound.
Underline the pictures whose names have the long **a** sound.

Skills: Using auditory discrimination skills; Understanding sound/symbol association;
Differentiating short and long vowel sounds

PHONICS SKILLS I

Initial consonant: **b**

Print the letters and words.

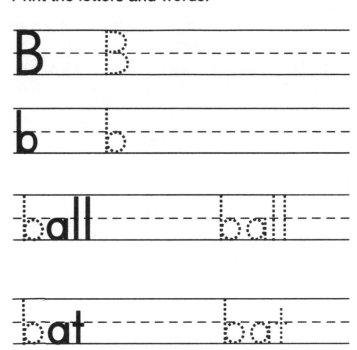

Finish the picture. Finish the word.

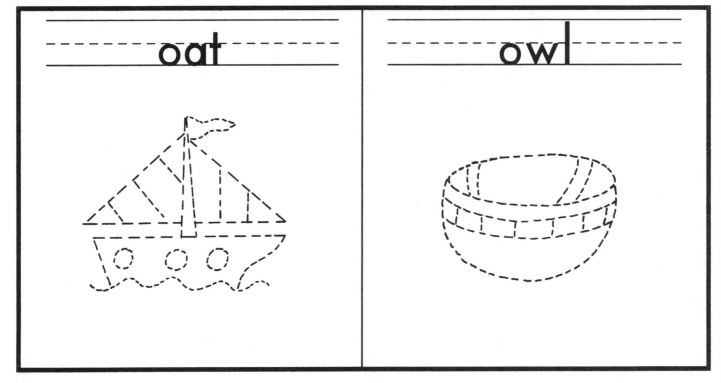

oat

owl

Skills: Recognition of the initial consonant "b"; Writing letters and words; Association between sounds, symbols, and words

PHONICS SKILLS I

Initial consonant: f

Print the letters and words.

F

f

fairy   fairy

fish   fish

Finish the picture. Finish the word.

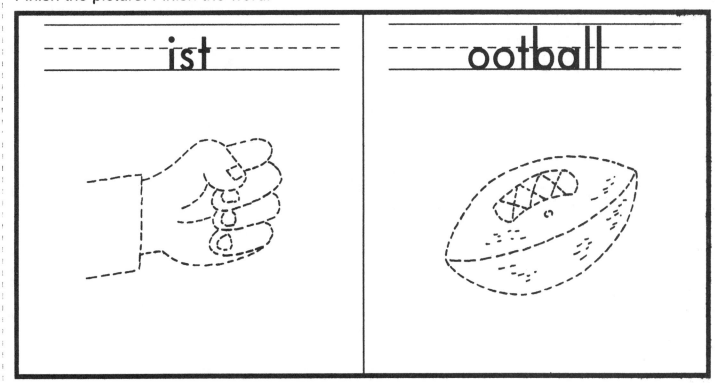

ist   ootball

Skills: Recognition of the initial consonant "f"; Writing letters and words; Association between sounds, symbols and words

Initial consonant: **g**

Print the letters and words.

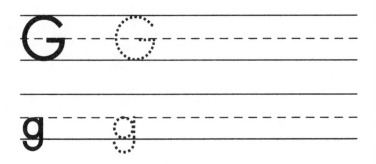

G - - - G - - - - - - -

g   g

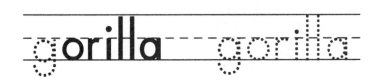

gorilla - - gorilla

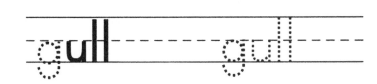

gull - - - gull

Finish the picture. Finish the word.

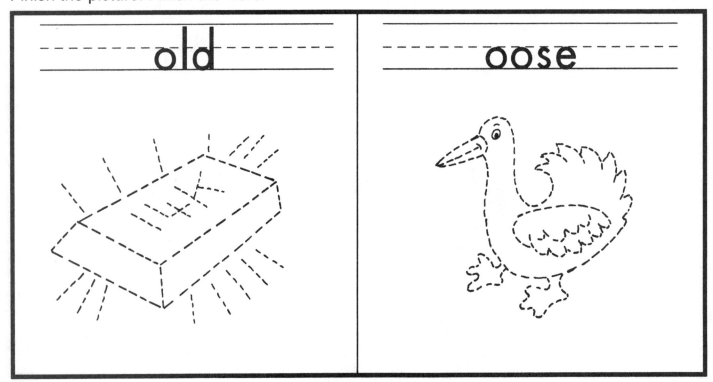

- - - - - old

oose

Skills: Recognition of the initial consonant "g"; Writing letters and words; Association between sounds, symbols, and words

PHONICS SKILLS I

Initial consonant: k

Print the letters and words.

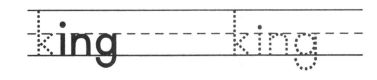

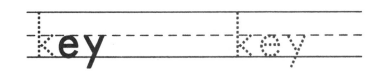

Finish the picture. Finish the word.

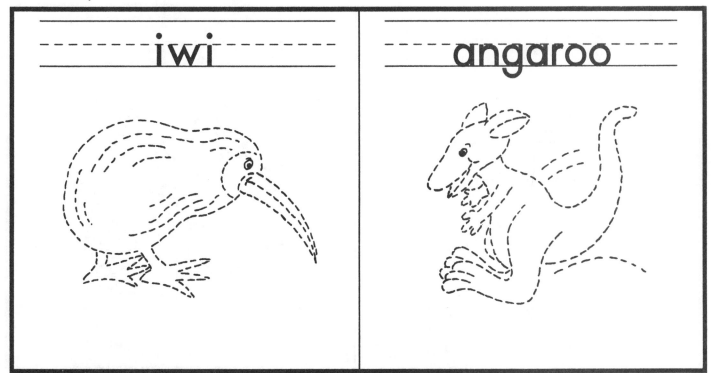

_iwi

_angaroo

Skills: Recognition of the initial consonant "k"; Writing letters and words; Association between sounds, symbols, and words

PHONICS SKILLS I

Initial consonant: **v**

Print the letters and words.

V   V

v   v

veil   veil

vest   vest

Finish the picture. Finish the word.

an

ane

Skills: Recognition of the initial consonant "v"; Writing letters and words; Association between sounds, symbols, and words

246

PHONICS SKILLS I

Initial consonant: **c**

Print the letters and words.

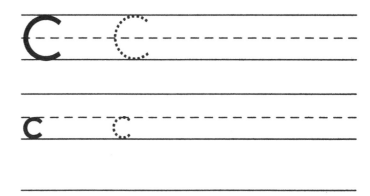

C   C

c   c

cone   cone

cow   cow

Finish the picture. Finish the word.

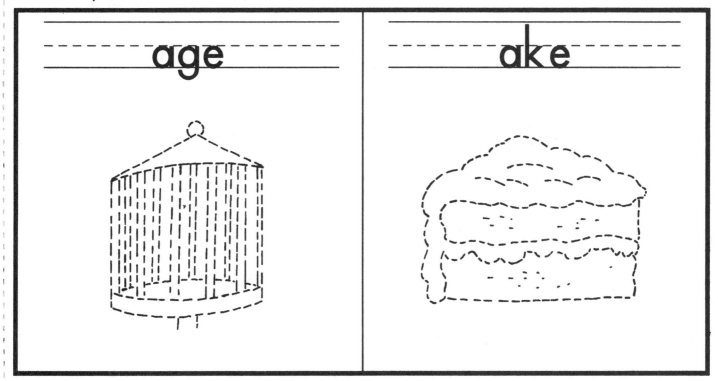

age

ake

Skills: Recognition of the initial consonant "c"; Writing letters and words; Association between sounds, symbols, and words

247

PHONICS SKILLS I

Initial consonant: h

Print the letters and words.

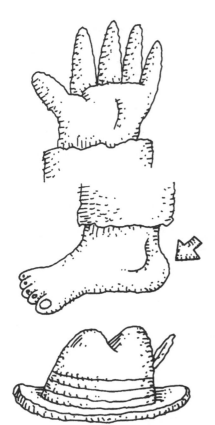

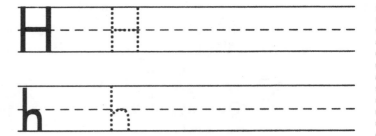

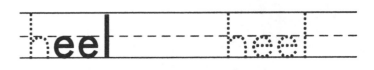

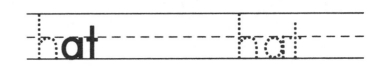

Finish the picture. Finish the word.

___og

___ouse

Skills: Recognition of the initial consonant "h"; Writing letters and words; Association between sounds, symbols and words

PHONICS SKILLS I

Initial consonant: **m**

Print the letters and words.

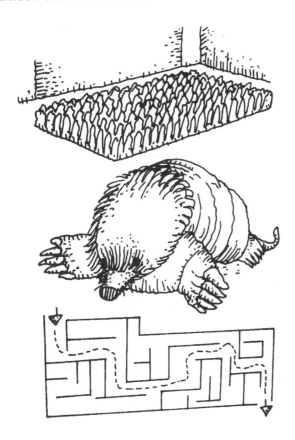

M M

m m

mole mole

maze maze

Finish the picture. Finish the word.

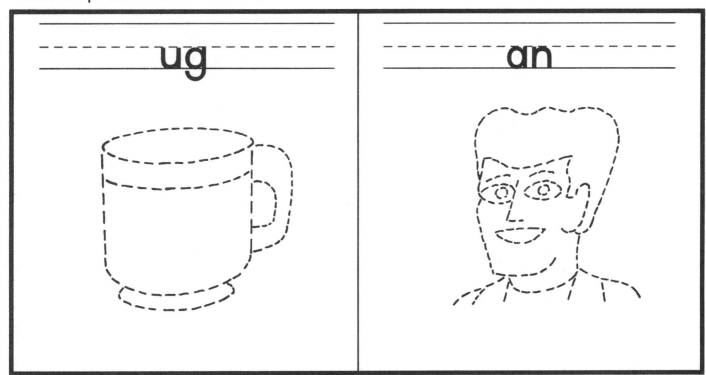

ug

an

Skills: Recognition of the initial consonant "m"; Writing letters and words; Association between sounds, symbols, and words

PHONICS SKILLS I

Initial consonant: **p**

Print the letters and words.

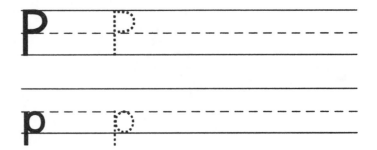

P   P

p   p

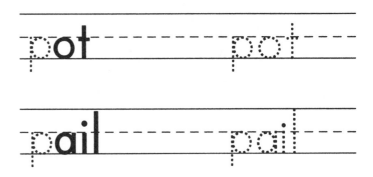

pot   pot

pail   pail

Finish the picture. Finish the word.

ig

aint

Skills: Recognition of the initial consonant "p"; Writing letters and words; Association between sounds, symbols, and words

PHONICS SKILLS I

Initial consonant: **y**

Print the letters and words.

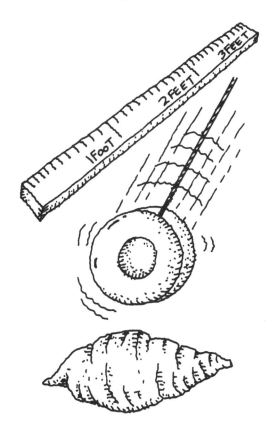

Y   Y

y   y

yo-yo   yo-yo

yam   yam

Finish the picture. Finish the word.

_arn

_ak

Skills: Recognition of the initial consonant "y"; Writing letters and words; Association between sounds, symbols, and words

PHONICS SKILLS I

Initial consonant: d

Print the letters and words.

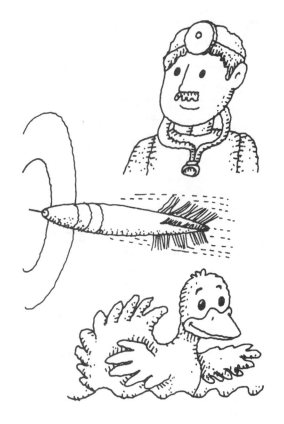

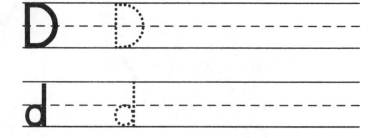

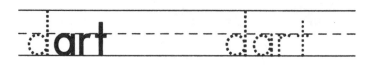

D

d

dart   dart

duck   duck

Finish the picture. Finish the word.

_____aisy

_____og

Skills: Recognition of the initial consonant "d"; Writing letters and words; Association between sounds, symbols, and words

PHONICS SKILLS I

Initial consonant: j

Print the letters and words.

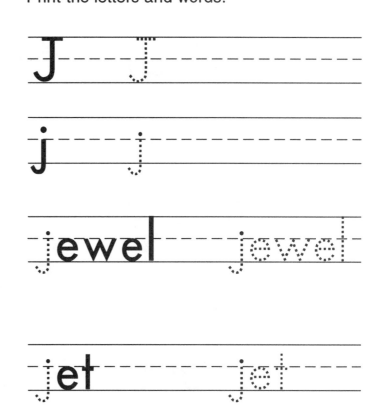

J   J

j   j

jewel   jewel

jet   jet

Finish the picture. Finish the word.

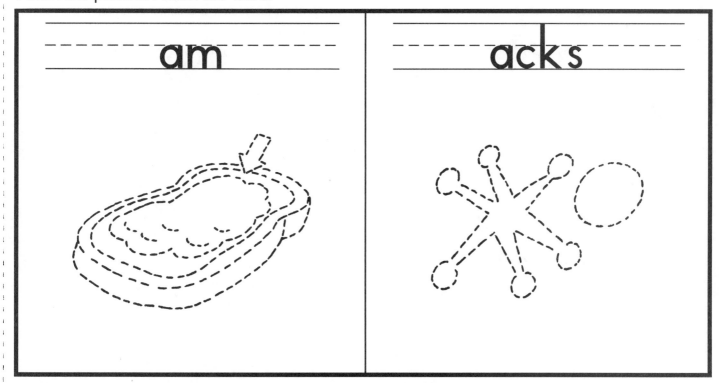

am

acks

Skills: Recognition of the initial consonant "j"; Writing letters and words; Association between sounds, symbols, and words

PHONICS SKILLS I

Initial consonant: **l**

Print the letters and words.

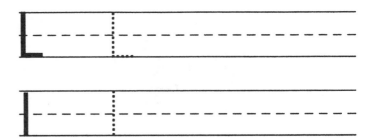

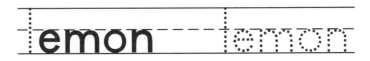

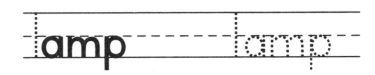

Finish the picture. Finish the word.

Skills: Recognition of the initial consonant "l"; Writing letters and words; Association between sounds, symbols, and words

PHONICS SKILLS I

Initial consonant: w

Print the letters and words.

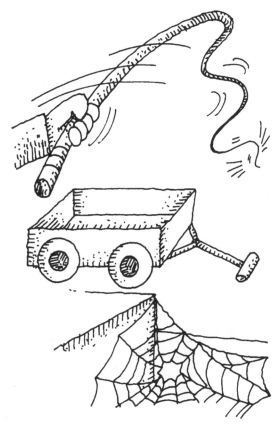

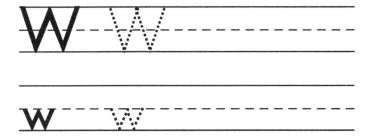

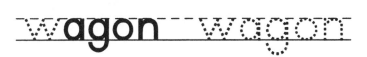

wagon   wagon

web   web

Finish the picture. Finish the word.

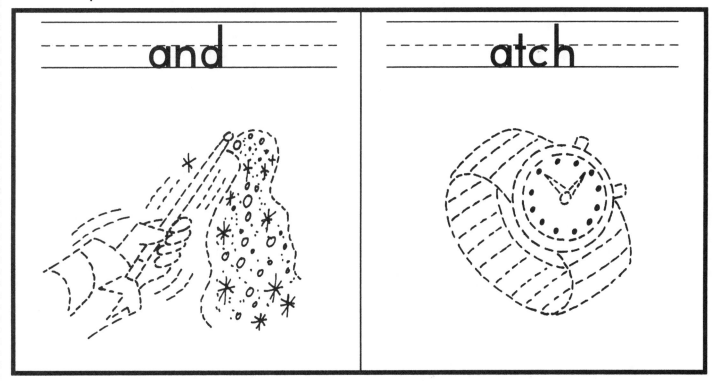

___ and   ___ atch

Skills: Recognition of the initial consonant "w"; Writing letters and words; Association between sounds, symbols, and words

PHONICS SKILLS I

Initial consonant: **z**

Print the letters and words.

Z   Z

z   z

zebra   zebra

zoom   zoom

Finish the picture. Finish the word.

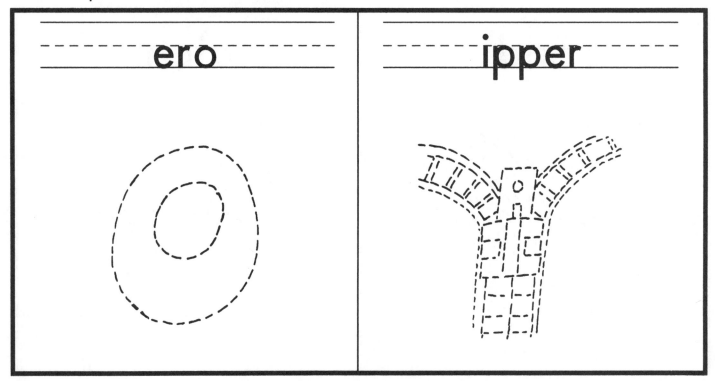

ero

ipper

Skills: Recognition of the initial consonant "z"; Writing letters and words; Association between sounds, symbols, and words

PHONICS SKILLS I

Initial consonant: **n**

Print the letters and words.

N N

n n

nest   nest

note   note

Finish the picture. Finish the word.

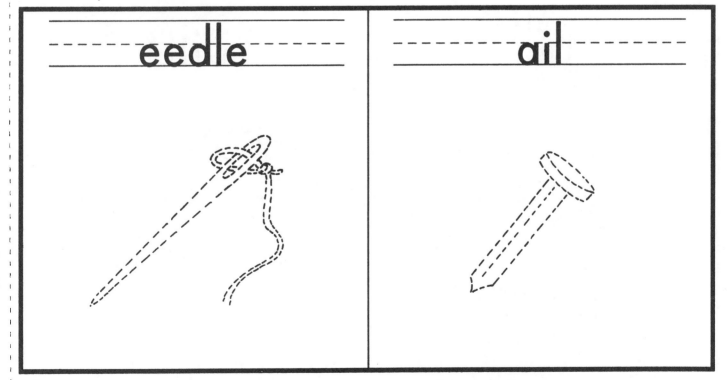

eedle   ail

Skills: Recognition of the initial consonant "n"; Writing letters and words; Association between sounds, symbols, and words

PHONICS SKILLS I

Initial consonant: q

Print the letters and words.

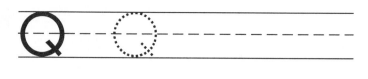

Q ⊙

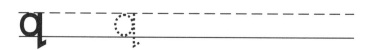

q q

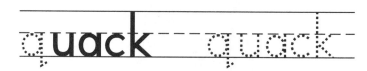

quack quack

quarter quarter

Finish the picture. Finish the word.

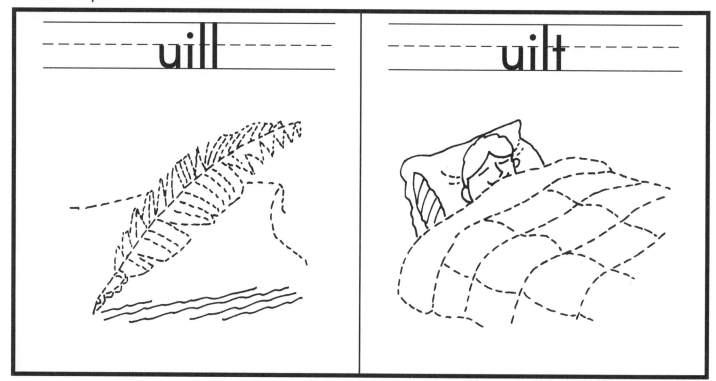

uill

uilt

Skills: Recognition of the initial consonant "q"; Writing letters and words; Association between sounds, symbols, and words

PHONICS SKILLS I

Initial consonant: **r**

Print the letters and words.

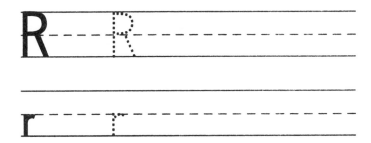

R   R

r   r

rose   rose

rattle   rattle

Finish the picture. Finish the word.

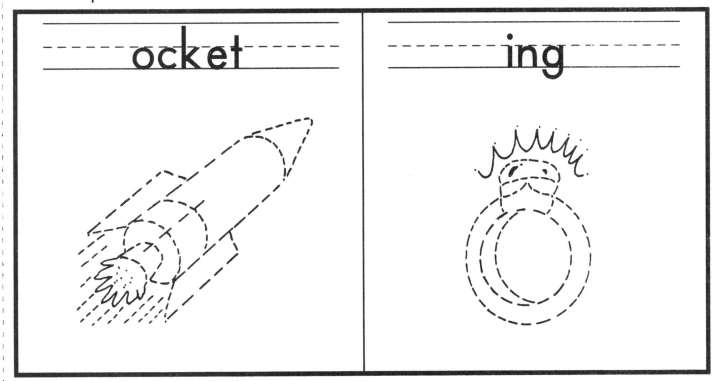

ocket

ing

Skills: Recognition of the initial consonant "r"; Writing letters and words; Association between sounds, symbols, and words

PHONICS SKILLS I

Initial consonant: **s**

Print the letters and words.

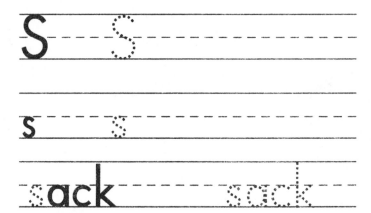

S   S

s   s

sack   sack

Santa   Santa

Finish the picture. Finish the word.

aw

ailor

Skills: Recognition of the initial consonant "s"; Writing letters and words; Association between sounds, symbols, and words

PHONICS SKILLS I

Initial Consonant: t

Print the letters and words.

T   T

t   t

tongue   tongue

tie   tie

Finish the picture. Finish the word.

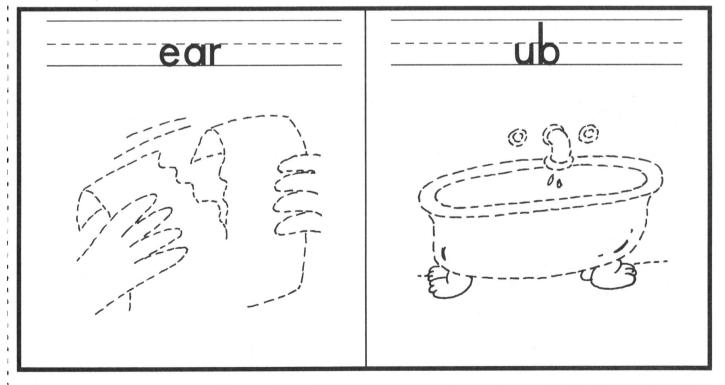

ear

ub

Skills: Recognition of the initial consonant "t"; Writing letters and words; Association between sounds, symbols, and words

PHONICS SKILLS I

Final consonant: b

cra**b**

b

Which ones end with **b**? Color them orange. Color the other pictures blue.

Skills: Recognition of the final consonant "b"; Auditory discrimination; Writing the letter "b"; Sound/symbol association

PHONICS SKILLS I

Final consonant: f

che

f

Which ones end with **f**? Color them red. Color the other pictures green.

Skills: Recognition of the final consonant "f"; Auditory discrimination; Writing the letter "f"; Sound/symbol association

PHONICS SKILLS I

Final consonant: d

s l e d

d

Which ones end with **d**? Color them yellow. Color the other pictures red.

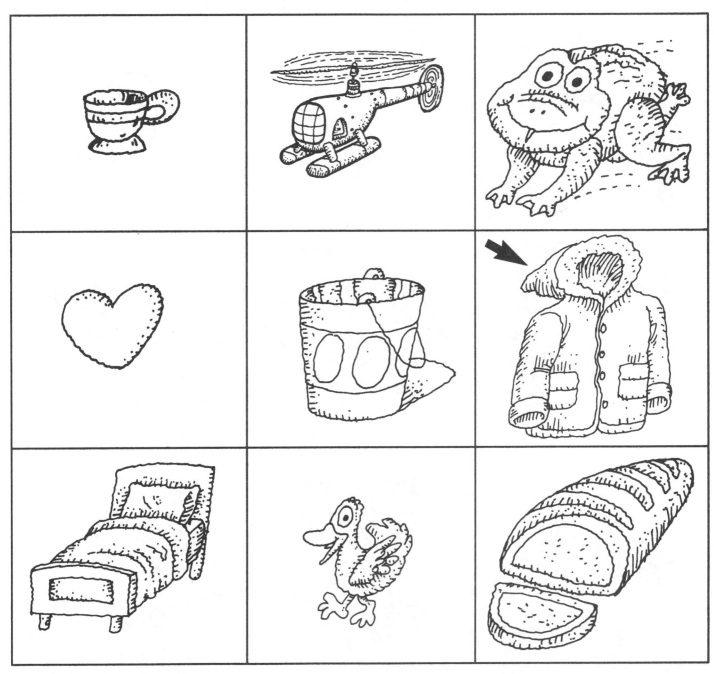

Skills: Recognition of the final consonant "d"; Auditory discrimination; Writing the letter "d"; Sound/symbol association

PHONICS SKILLS I

Final consonant: g

do g

g g

Which ones end with **g**? Color them brown. Color the other pictures blue.

Skills: Recognition of the final consonant "g"; Auditory discrimination; Writing the letter "g"; Sound/symbol association

PHONICS SKILLS I

Final consonant: k

SOC k

k

Which ones end with **k**? Color them blue. Color the other pictures red.

Skills: Recognition of the final consonant "k"; Auditory discrimination; Writing the letter "k"; Sound/symbol association

PHONICS SKILLS I

Final consonant: **m**

dru m

m m

Which ones end with **m**? Color them orange. Color the other pictures red.

Skills: Recognition of the final consonant "m"; Auditory discrimination; Writing the letter "m"; Sound/symbol association

PHONICS SKILLS I

Final consonant: l

pai

l

Which ones end with l? Color them red. Color the other pictures blue.

Skills: Recognition of the final consonant "l"; Auditory discrimination; Writing the letter "l"; Sound/symbol association

PHONICS SKILLS I

Final consonant: **n**

ma**n**

n

Which ones end with **n**? Color them green. Color the other pictures yellow.

Skills: Recognition of the final consonant "n"; Auditory discrimination; Writing the letter "n"; Sound/symbol association

PHONICS SKILLS I

Final consonant: **p**

mop

p

Which ones end with **p**? Color them red. Color the other pictures green.

Skills: Recognition of the final consonant "p"; Auditory discrimination; Writing the letter "p";
Sound/symbol association

Final consonant: r

bear

r

Which ones end with **r**? Color them brown. Color the other pictures green.

Skills: Recognition of the final consonant "r"; Auditory discrimination; Writing the letter "r"; Sound/symbol association

PHONICS SKILLS I

Final consonant: t

boa‡

t

Which ones end with **t**? Color them yellow. Color the other pictures blue.

Skills: Recognition of the final consonant "t"; Auditory discrimination; Writing the letter "t"; Sound/symbol association

PHONICS SKILLS I

Final consonant: **x**

fo x

x x

Which ones end with **x**? Color them green. Color the other pictures brown.

Skills: Recognition of the final consonant "x"; Auditory discrimination; Writing the letter "x"; Sound/symbol association

PHONICS SKILLS II

Short vowel: ă

Print the letters and words.

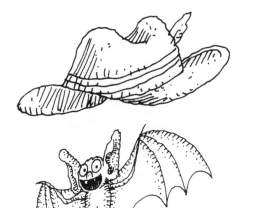

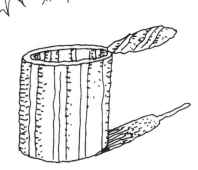

A   A

a   a

bat   bat

can   can

Finish the picture. Finish the word.

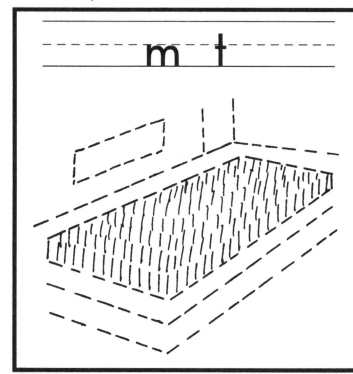

m t

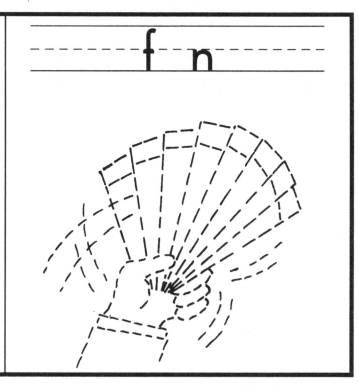

f n

Skills: Recognition of the short vowel "a"; Writing letters and words; Association between sounds, symbols, and words

PHONICS SKILLS II

Short vowel: ă

A   A

a   a

Which ones have the ă sound? Color them blue. Color the other pictures green.

Skills: Recognition of the short vowel "a"; Auditory discrimination; Writing the letter "a";
Sound/symbol association

PHONICS SKILLS II

Short vowel: ĕ

Print the letters and words.

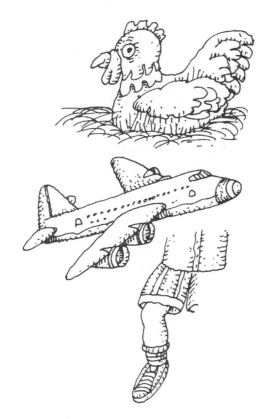

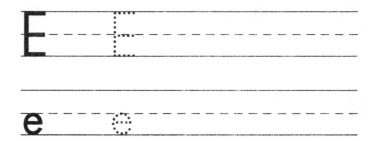

E   E

e   e

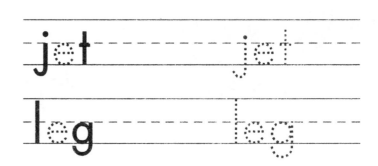

jet   jet

leg   leg

Finish the picture. Finish the word.

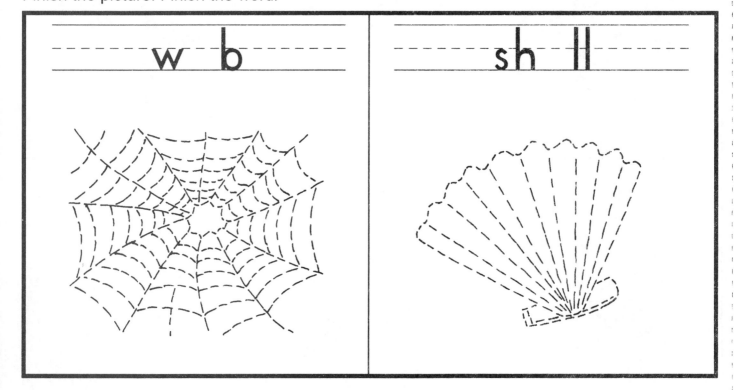

w b   sh ll

Skills: Recognition of the short vowel "e"; Writing letters and words; Association between sounds, symbols, and words

PHONICS SKILLS II

Short vowel: ĕ

E ‑‑ E‑‑

e ⋅⋅

Which ones have the ĕ sound? Color them blue. Color the other pictures yellow.

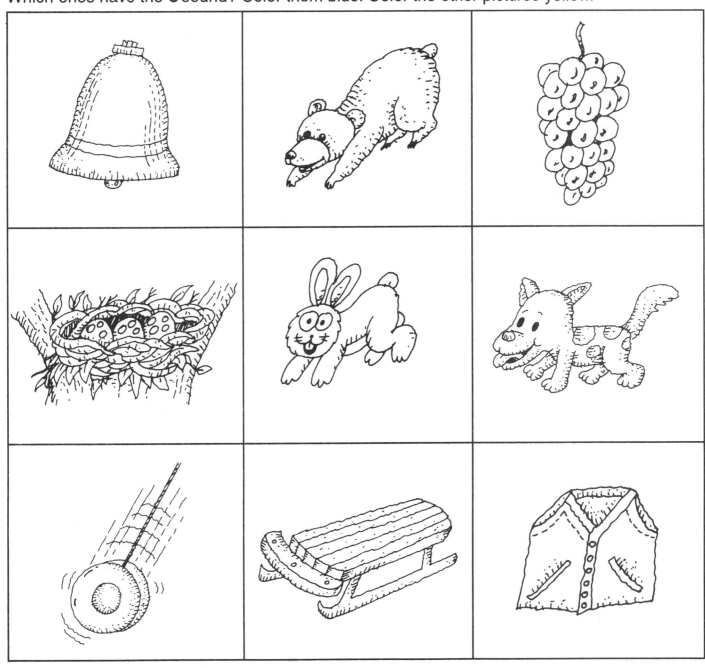

Skills: Recognition of the short vowel "e"; Auditory discrimination; Writing the letter "e"; Sound/symbol association

PHONICS SKILLS II

Short vowel: ĭ

Print the letters and words.

I   I

i   i

hill   hill

pig   pig

Finish the picture. Finish the word.

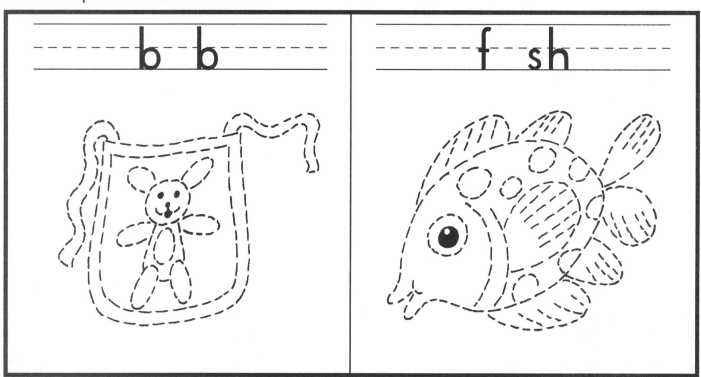

b__b

f__sh

Skills: Recognition of the short vowel "i"; Writing letters and words; Association between sounds, symbols, and words

PHONICS SKILLS II

Short vowel: ĭ

I I

i i

Which have the ĭ sound? Color them green. Color the other pictures brown.

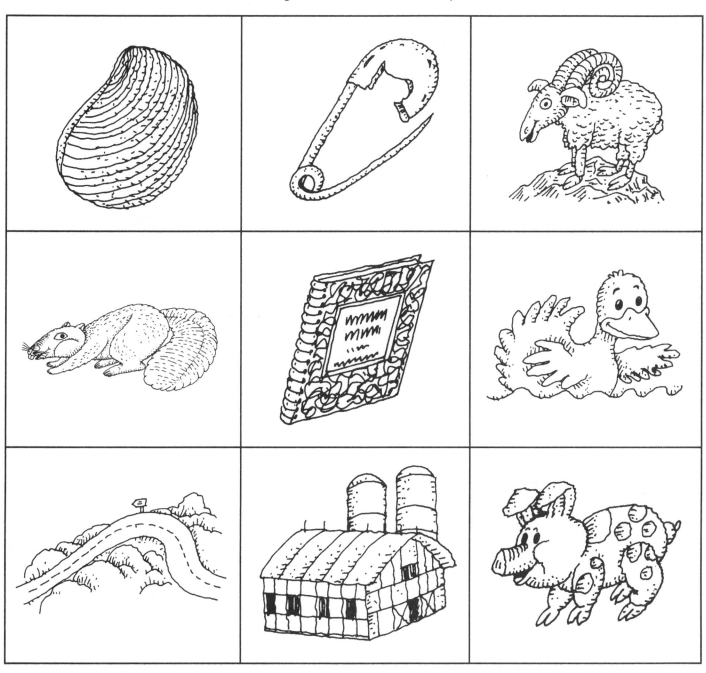

Skills: Recognition of the short vowel "i"; Auditory discrimination; Writing the letter "i"; Sound/symbol association

PHONICS SKILLS II

Short vowel: ŏ

Print the letters and words.

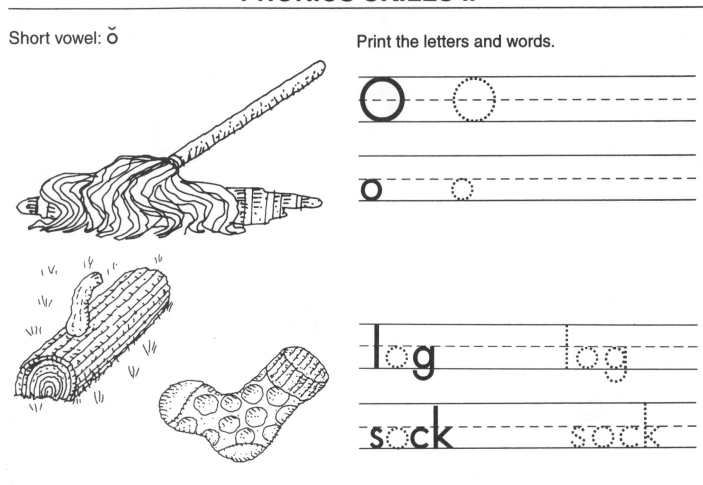

Finish the picture. Finish the word.

Skills: Recognition of the short vowel "o"; Writing letters and words; Association between sounds, symbols, and words

PHONICS SKILLS II

Short vowel: ŏ

Which have the ŏ sound? Color them orange. Color the other pictures green.

Skills: Recognition of the short vowel "o"; Auditory discrimination; Writing the letter "o"; Sound/symbol association

PHONICS SKILLS II

Short vowel: ŭ

Print the letters and words.

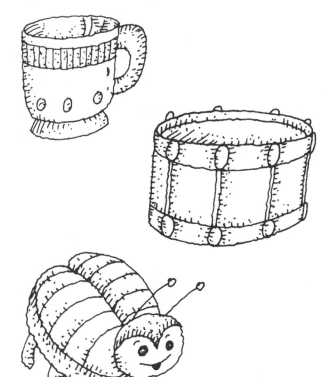

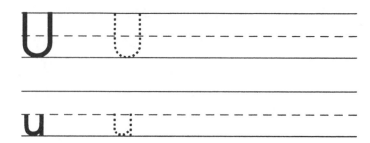

U   U

u   u

drum   drum

bug   bug

Finish the picture. Finish the word.

t b   d ck

Skills: Recognition of the short vowel "u"; Writing letters and words; Association between sounds, symbols, and words

PHONICS SKILLS II

Short vowel: ŭ

U ⌐‾‾‾‾‾‾‾‾‾‾‾‾‾‾‾‾‾‾‾‾‾‾‾

u ⌐‾‾‾‾‾‾‾‾‾‾‾‾‾‾‾‾‾‾‾‾‾‾‾

Which have the ŭ sound? Color them red. Color the other pictures yellow.

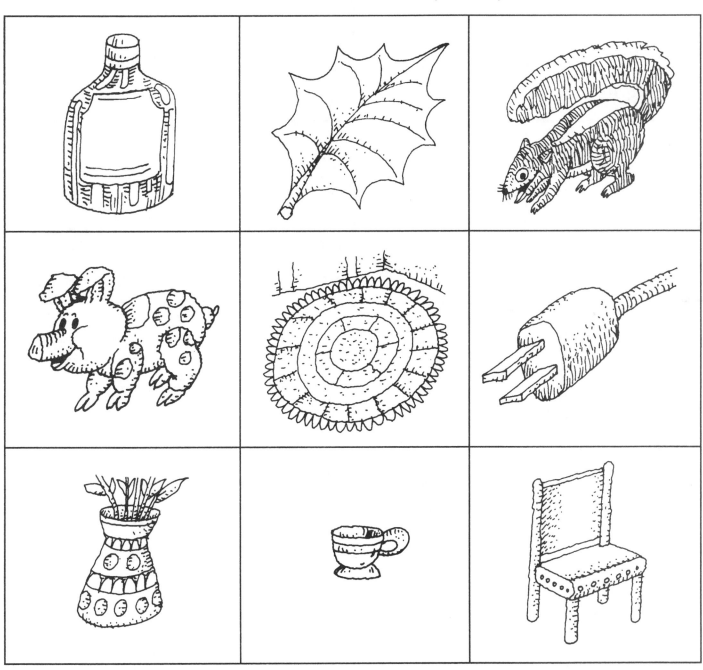

Skills: Recognition of the short vowel "u"; Auditory discrimination; Writing the letter "u"; Sound/symbol association

PHONICS SKILLS II

Short vowels: ă, ĕ, ĭ, ŏ, ŭ

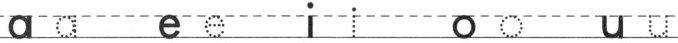

Say the name of each picture. Listen to the vowel sound. Then circle the vowel and print the letter.

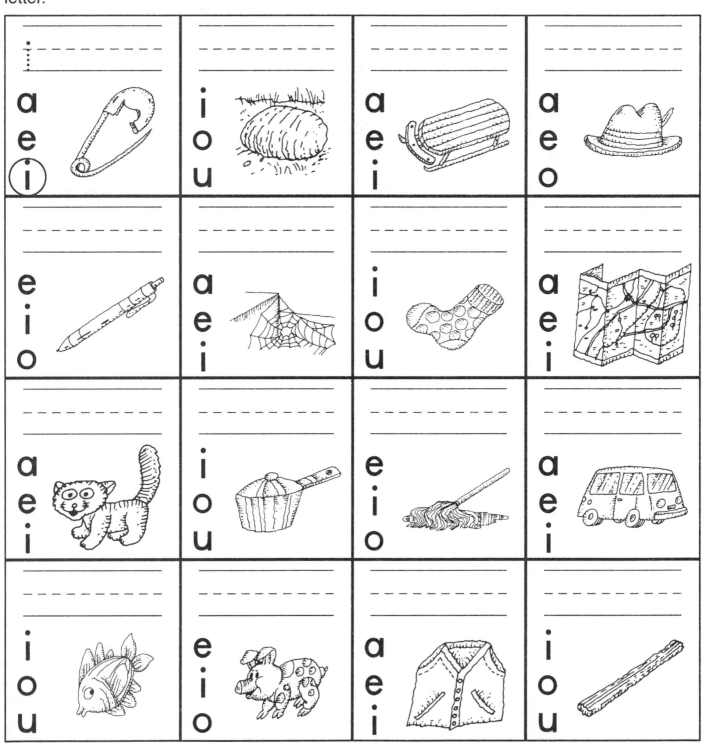

Skills: Recognition of the short vowel sounds; Writing letters; Auditory and visual discrimination

PHONICS SKILLS II

Long vowel: ā

Print the letters and words.

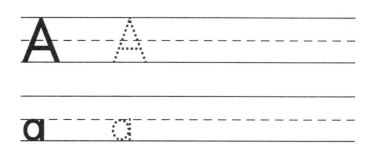

A   A

a   a

mane   mane

cape   cape

Finish the picture. Finish the word.

r   ke

c   ke

Skills: Recognition of the long vowel "a"; Writing letters and words; Association between sounds, symbols, and words

PHONICS SKILLS II

Long vowel: ā

A   A

a   a

Which ones have the ā sound? Color them red. Color the other pictures blue.

Skills: Recognition of the long vowel "a"; Auditory discrimination; Writing the letter "a"; Sound/symbol association

PHONICS SKILLS II

Long vowel: ē

Print the letters and words.

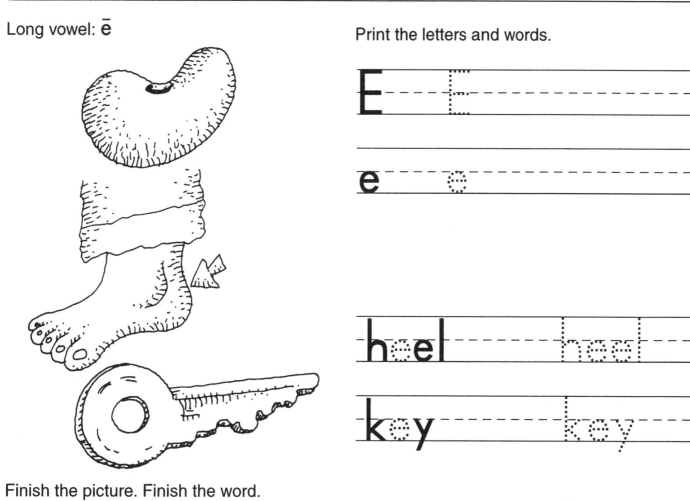

E   E

e   e

heel   heel

key   key

Finish the picture. Finish the word.

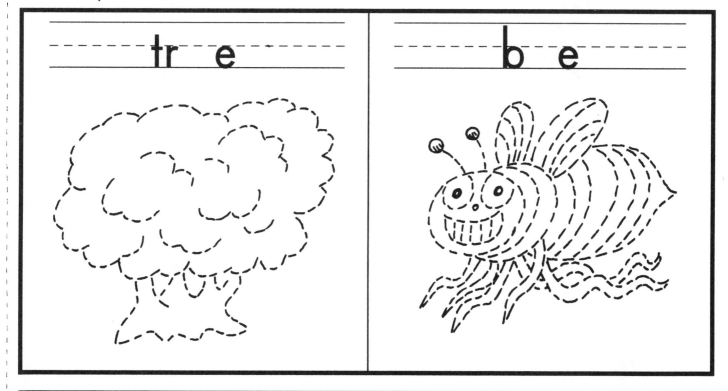

tr _ e   b _ e

Skills: Recognition of the long vowel "e"; Writing letters and words; Association between sounds, symbols, and words

PHONICS SKILLS II

Long vowel: ē

E - - - - - - - - - -

e - - - - -

Which ones have the ē sound? Color them green. Color the other pictures blue.

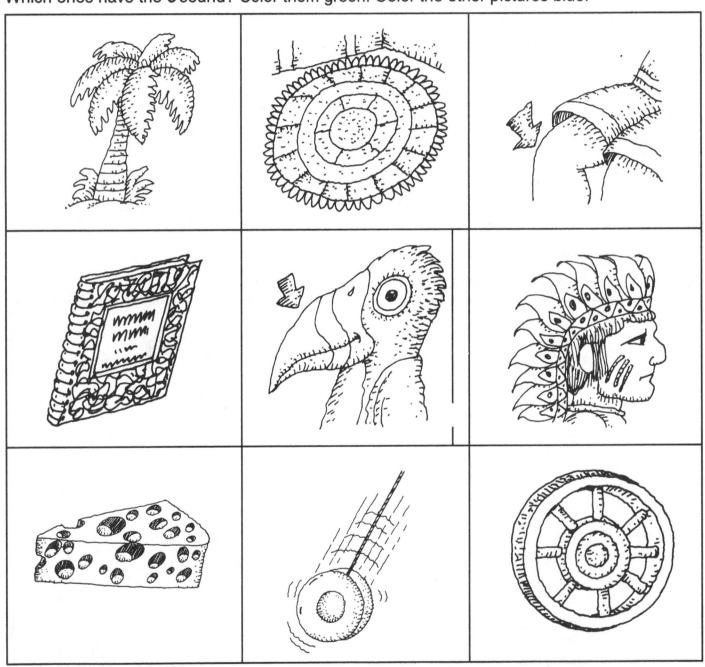

Skills: Recognition of the long vowel "e"; Auditory discrimination; Writing the letter "e"; Sound/symbol association

PHONICS SKILLS II

Long vowel: ī

Print the letters and words.

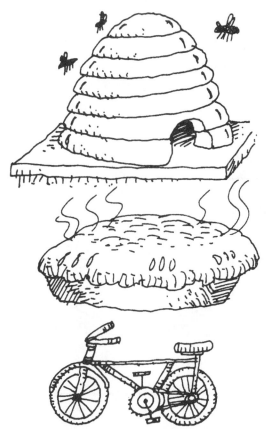

I   I

i   i

pie   pie

bike   bike

Finish the picture. Finish the word.

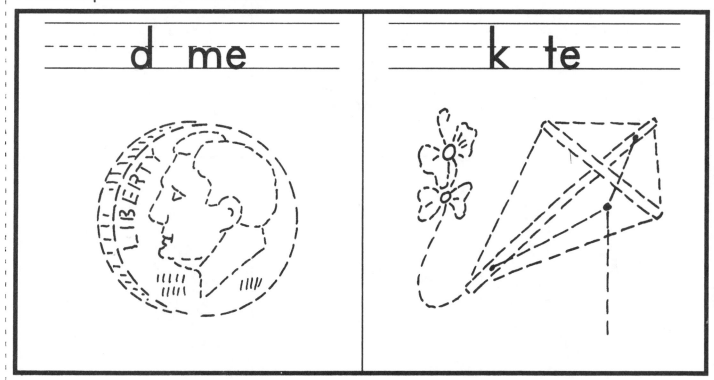

d me

k te

Skills: Recognition of the long vowel "i"; Writing letters and words; Association between sounds, symbols, and words

PHONICS SKILLS II

Long vowel: ī

I

i   i

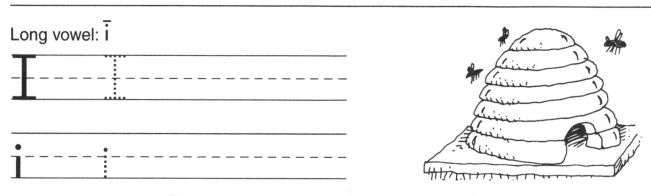

Which ones have the ī sound? Color them yellow. Color the other pictures red.

Skills: Recognition of the long vowel "i"; Auditory discrimination; Writing the letter "i"; Sound/symbol association

PHONICS SKILLS II

Long vowel: ō

Print the letters and words.

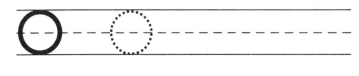

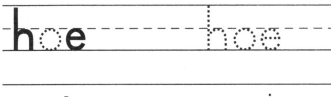

hoe   hoe

note   note

Finish the picture. Finish the word.

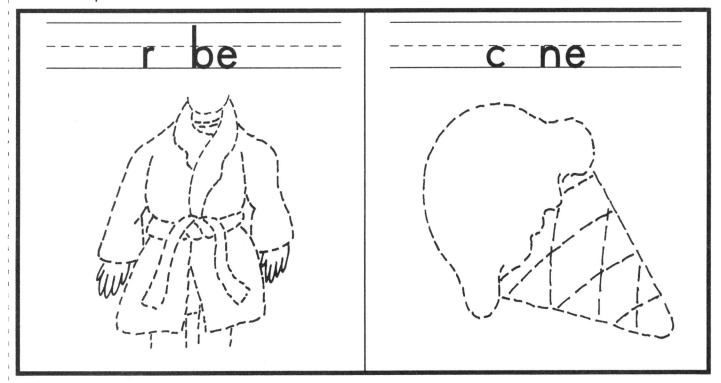

r be   c ne

Skills: Recognition of the long vowel "o"; Writing letters and words; Association between sounds, symbols, and words

PHONICS SKILLS II

Long vowel: ō

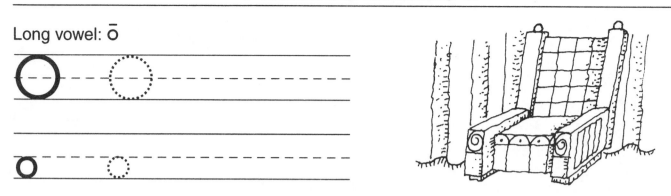

Which ones have the ō sound? Color them brown. Color the other pictures blue.

Skills: Recognition of the long vowel "o"; Auditory discrimination; Writing the letter "o"; Sound/symbol association

PHONICS SKILLS II

Long vowel: ū

Print the letters and words.

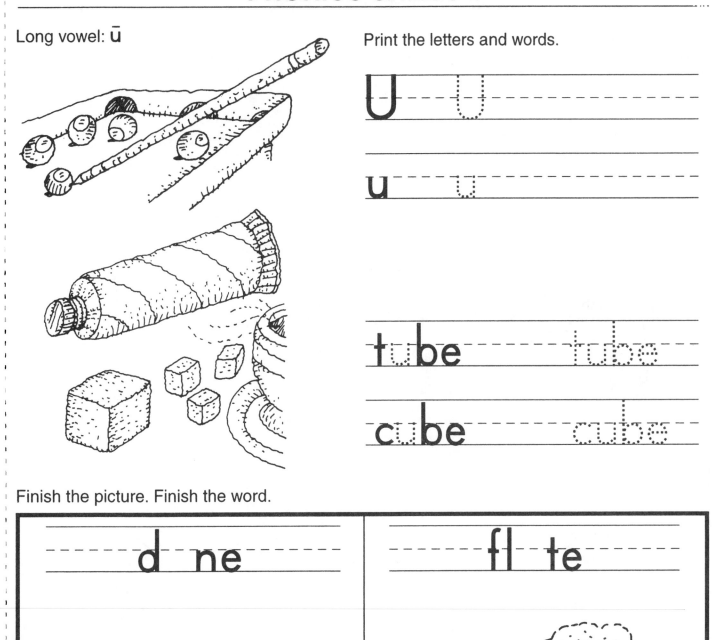

U   U

u   u

tube   tube

cube   cube

Finish the picture. Finish the word.

d ne

fl te

Skills: Recognition of the long vowel "u"; Writing letters and words; Association between sounds, symbols, and words

PHONICS SKILLS II

Long vowel: ū

U U

u u

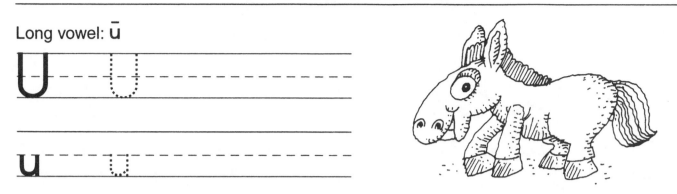

Which ones have the ū sound? Color them green. Color the other pictures red.

Skills: Recognition of the long vowel "u"; Auditory discrimination; Writing the letter "u"; Sound/symbol association

PHONICS SKILLS II

Long vowels: ā, ē, ī, ō, ū

a a   e e   i i   o o   u u

Say the name of each picture. Listen to the vowel sound. Then circle the vowel and print the letter.

Skills: Recognition of the long vowel sounds; Writing letters; Auditory and visual discrimination

PHONICS SKILLS II

Long and short vowel: a

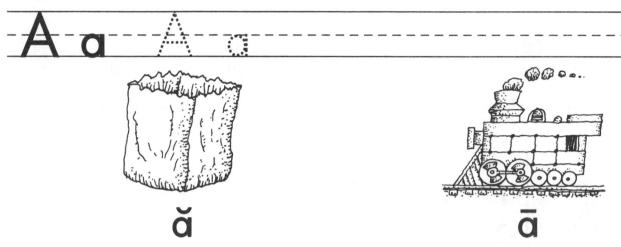

ă   ā

Which ones have the ă sound? Color them red.
Which ones have the ā sound? Color them blue.

Skills: Auditory and visual discrimination; Sound/symbol association; Writing the letter "a"

PHONICS SKILLS II

Long and short vowel: **e**

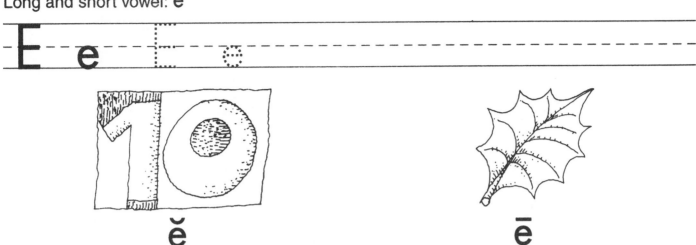

ĕ   ē

Which ones have the ĕ sound? Color them green.
Which ones have the ē sound? Color them yellow.

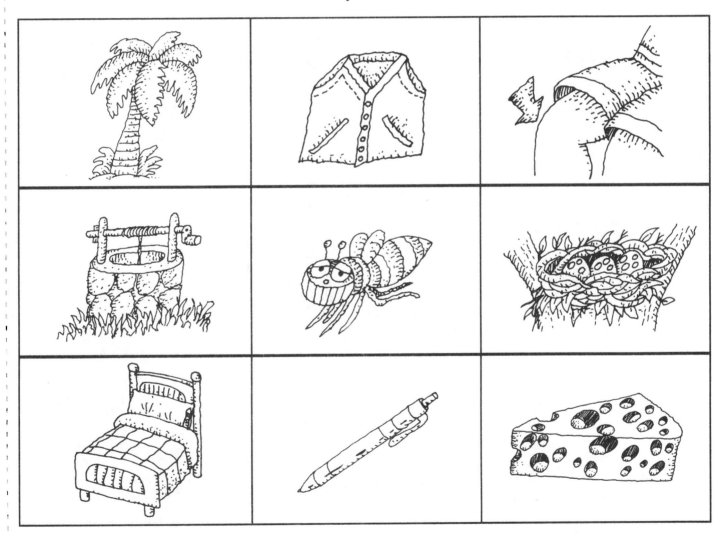

Skills: Auditory and visual discrimination; Sound/symbol association; Writing the letter "e"

PHONICS SKILLS II

Long and short vowel: **i**

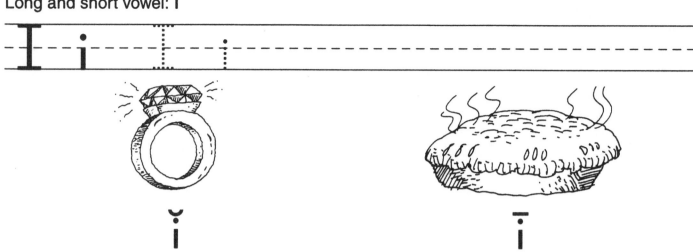

Which ones have the **ĭ** sound? Color them orange.
Which ones have the **ī** sound? Color them yellow.

Skills: Auditory and visual discrimination; Sound/symbol association; Writing the letter "i"

PHONICS SKILLS II

Long and short vowel: o

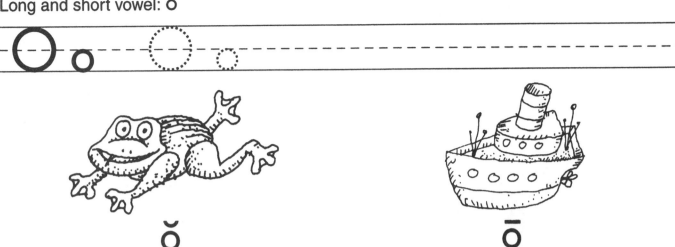

Which ones have the ŏ sound? Color them blue.
Which ones have the ō sound? Color them green.

Skills: Auditory and visual discrimination; Sound/symbol association; Writing the letter "o"

PHONICS SKILLS II

Long and short vowel: **u**

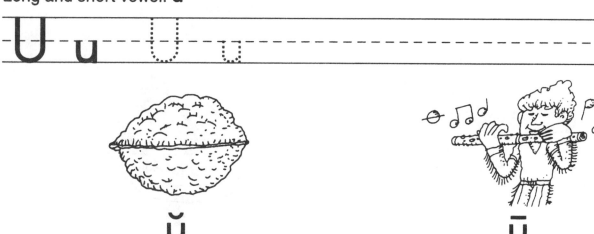

ŭ   ū

Which ones have the ŭ sound? Color them green.
Which ones have the ū sound? Color them red.

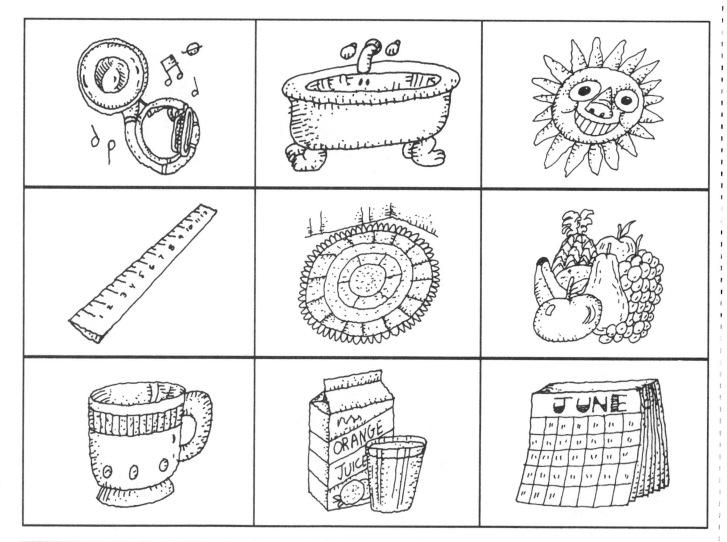

Skills: Auditory and visual discrimination; Sound/symbol association; Writing the letter "u"

PHONICS SKILLS II

Long and short vowels: a , e , i , o , u

a a   e e   i i   o o   u u

Say the name of each picture. Listen to the vowel sound. Then print the vowel you hear.

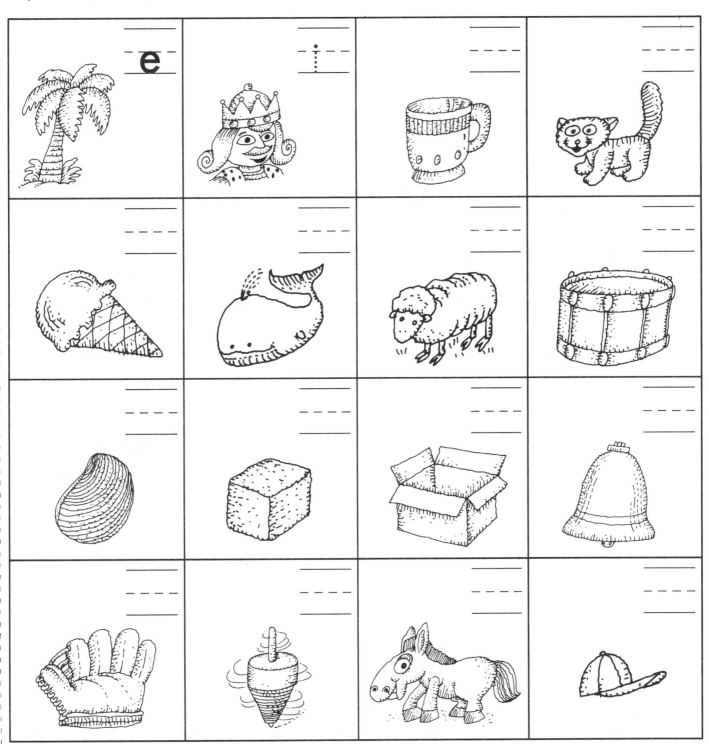

Skills: Recognition of the long and short vowel sounds; Writing letters; Auditory and visual discrimination

PHONICS SKILLS II

Initial consonant blends: cl, cr

cl _____

cr _____

Which ones begin with **cl**? Color them blue.
Which ones begin with **cr**? Color them green.

Skills: Understanding that some consonant sounds can be blended together; Sound/symbol association

PHONICS SKILLS II

Initial consonant blends: **bl, br**

b̶l̶‑‑‑‑‑‑‑‑‑‑‑‑‑‑‑‑‑‑‑‑‑‑‑‑‑‑‑‑‑‑

b̶r̶‑‑‑‑‑‑‑‑‑‑‑‑‑‑‑‑‑‑‑‑‑‑‑‑‑‑‑‑‑‑

Which ones begin with **bl**? Color them black.
Which ones begin with **br**? Color them brown.

Skills: Understanding that some consonant sounds can be blended together; Sound/symbol association

PHONICS SKILLS II

Initial consonant blends: dr, tr

d r

t r

Which ones begin with **dr**? Color them blue.
Which ones begin with **tr**? Color them red.

Skills: Understanding that some consonant sounds can be blended together; Sound/symbol association

PHONICS SKILLS II

Initial consonant blends: sk, sl

Which ones begin with **sk**? Color them yellow.
Which ones begin with **sl**? Color them red.

Skills: Understanding that some consonant sounds can be blended together; Sound/symbol association

PHONICS SKILLS II

Initial consonant blends: sp, st

sp _

st _

Which ones begin with **sp**? Color them yellow.
Which ones begin with **st**? Color them orange.

Skills: Understanding that some consonant sounds can be blended together; Sound/symbol association

PHONICS SKILLS II

Initial consonant blends: fl, fr

Print the letters and words.

fr fr

fl fl

flame flame

frame frame

Finish the picture. Finish the word.

og

ower

Skills: Understanding that some consonant sounds can be blended together; Sound/symbol association

PHONICS SKILLS II

Initial consonant blends: g**l**, g**r**

Print the letters and words.

gr ⌐gr⌐

gl ⌐gl⌐

grill ⌐grill⌐

glove ⌐glove⌐

Finish the picture. Finish the word.

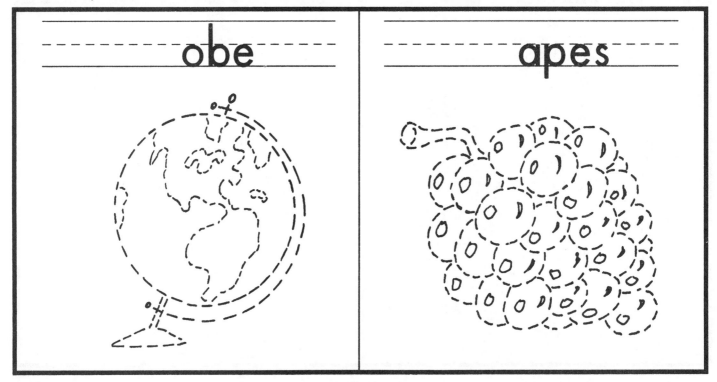

obe

apes

Skills: Understanding that some consonant sounds can be blended together; Sound/symbol association

PHONICS SKILLS II

Initial consonant blends: pl, pr

Print the letters and words.

pl   p̣ḷ

pr   p̣r̈

p̣lant   p̣ḷant

p̣rize   p̣rize

Finish the picture. Finish the word.

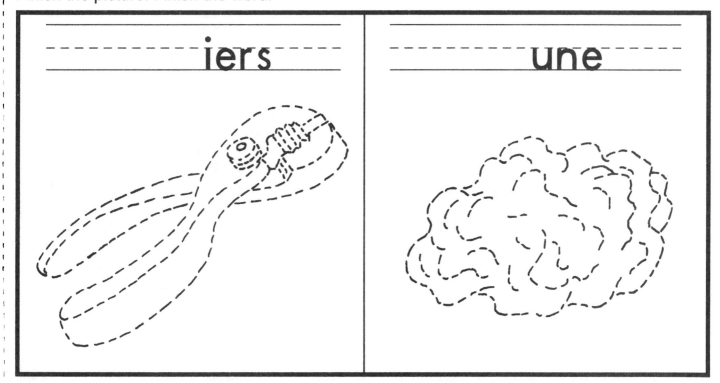

iers

une

Skills: Understanding that some consonant sounds can be blended together; Sound/symbol association

PHONICS SKILLS II

Initial consonant blends: sn, sw

Print the letters and words.

sn   sn

sw   sw

snore   snore

swan   swan

Finish the picture. Finish the word.

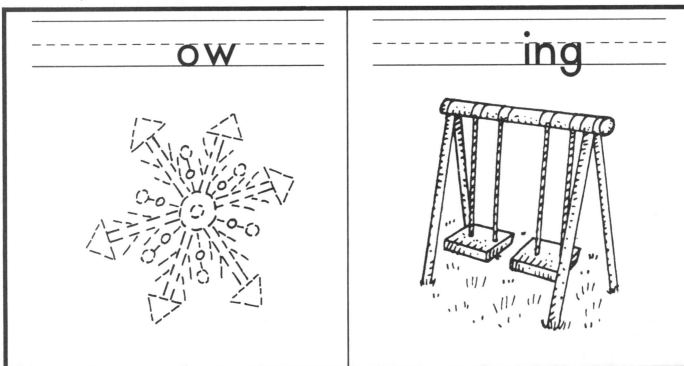

ow

ing

Skills: Understanding that some consonant sounds can be blended together; Sound/symbol association

PHONICS SKILLS II

Initial consonant blends: c r , f r , p r , t r

cr   fr   pr   tr

Say the name of each picture. Circle the two letters you hear at the beginning.
Then print the letters.

cr cl tr	cr tr fr	fr fl pr
fl fr cr	ch th fr	cr th wh
fr tr pr	cl cr tr	cl tr pr

Skills: Recognition of consonant blends; Writing letters; Auditory and visual discrimination

PHONICS SKILLS II

Consonant digraph: ch

ch   ch

ch

Which ones begin with **ch**? Color them brown. Color the other pictures red.

Skills: Recognizing and understanding consonant digraphs; Sound/symbol association

PHONICS SKILLS II

Consonant digraph: sh

sh sh

sh

Which ones begin with **sh**? Color them orange. Color the other pictures green.

Skills: Recognizing and understanding consonant digraphs; Sound/symbol association

PHONICS SKILLS II

Consonant digraph: th

th - - th

th

Which ones begin with **th**? Color them blue. Color the other pictures red.

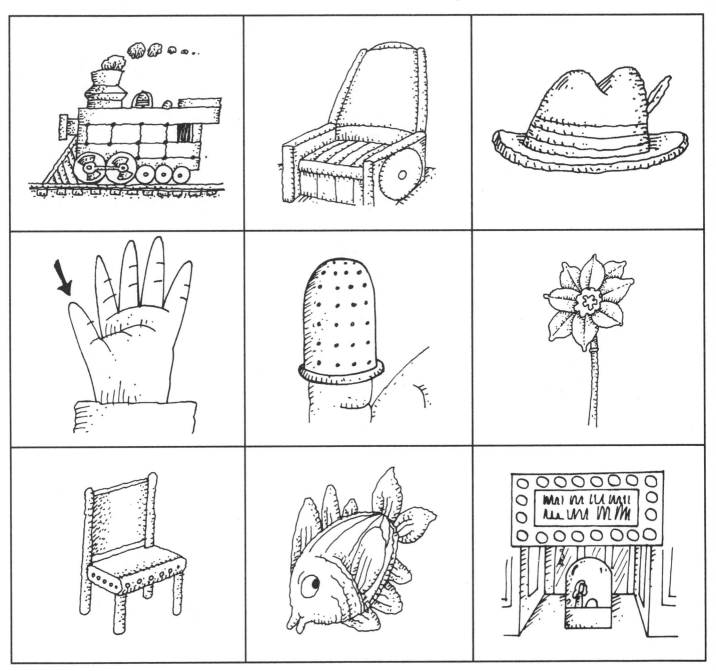

Skills: Recognizing and understanding consonant digraphs; Sound/symbol association

PHONICS SKILLS II

Consonant digraph: wh

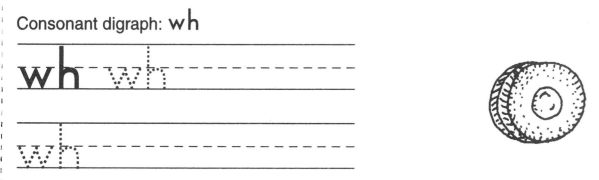

wh wh ------------------------------

wh ------------------------------

Which ones begin with **wh**? Color them yellow. Color the other pictures blue.

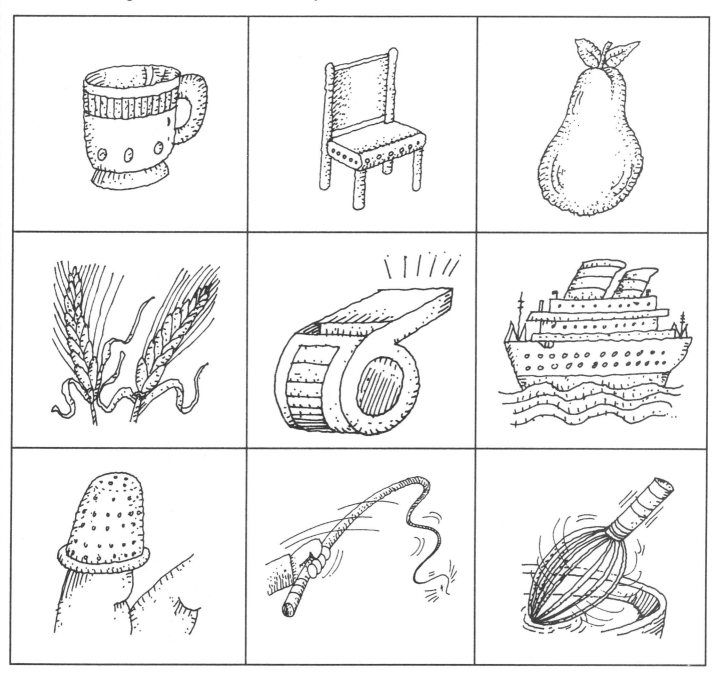

Skills: Recognizing and understanding consonant digraphs; Sound/symbol association

PHONICS SKILLS II

Consonant digraphs: c h , s h , t h , w h

ch ——— sh ——— th ——— wh

Say the name of each picture. Circle the two letters you hear at the beginning.
Then print the letters.

sh th th wh	ch sh th	ch sh wh	ch th wh
ch sh wh	sh ch wh	sh th wh	sh th wh
sh th wh	ch sh wh	ch th wh	ch sh th
sh th wh	sh ch wh	ch sh th	ch sh wh

Skills: Recognition of consonant digraphs; Auditory and visual discrimination; Writing letters

316

ACHIEVEMENT CHECKLIST

Use the checklist below after each session with this book. If your child had trouble with a page, find the problem skill and list the page number in the middle column. You'll want to return to it later. If your child successfully completed the pages containing a skill, put a check mark in the "Mastered" column. Your child can watch with pride as the column fills up with skills he or she has mastered.

BASIC SKILLS	Needs Work	Mastered!
HANDWRITING		
Tracing		
Fine motor skill development		
Eye / hand coordination		
Forming closed curves		
Forming open curves		
Forming vertical lines		
Forming diagonal lines		
Forming horizontal lines		
Forming upper / lowercase Aa		
Forming upper / lowercase Bb		
Forming upper / lowercase Cc		
Forming upper / lowercase Dd		
Forming upper / lowercase Ee		
Forming upper / lowercase Ff		
Forming upper / lowercase Gg		
Forming upper / lowercase Hh		
Forming upper / lowercase Ii		
Forming upper / lowercase Jj		
Forming upper / lowercase Kk		
Forming upper / lowercase Ll		
Forming upper / lowercase Mm		
Forming upper / lowercase Nn		
Forming upper / lowercase Oo		
Forming upper / lowercase Pp		
Forming upper / lowercase Qq		
Forming upper / lowercase Rr		

BASIC SKILLS	Needs Work	Mastered!
Forming upper / lowercase Ss		
Forming upper / lowercase Tt		
Forming upper / lowercase Uu		
Forming upper / lowercase Vv		
Forming upper / lowercase Ww		
Forming upper / lowercase Xx		
Forming upper / lowercase Yy		
Forming upper / lowercase Zz		
COLORS, SHAPES, AND NUMBERS		
Writing color words		
Distinguishing color		
Classification		
Word recognition		
Sight vocabulary		
Shape recognition		
Recognizing sets and numerals		
Forming numerals 1–10		
Recognizing number words		
BASIC MATH SKILLS		
Ordering numbers to 25		
Adding groups of objects		
Understanding addition sentences		
Solving addition problems		
Subtracting groups of objects		
Counting		
Forming groups		
Observing and continuing patterns		
One-to-one correspondence		
Matching		
Understanding greater / less than		
Creating sets		
Recognizing ordinal numbers		
Comparing weight		
Comparing height		

BASIC SKILLS	Needs Work	Mastered!
Comparing length		
Measuring		
TIME AND MONEY		
Time awareness		
Telling time		
Showing time on a clock		
Money awareness		
READING READINESS		
Distinguishing upper / lowercase letters		
Association / classification		
Logical reasoning		
Visual discrimination		
Recognizing right and left		
Auditory discrimination		
Visual memory		
Recognizing similarities and differences		
Noticing details		
Spatial awareness		
Recognizing letters		
Vocabulary		
Sequencing		
Problem solving		
Predicting		
Understanding story order		
PHONICS SKILLS I and II		
Letter / sound relationships		
Beginning sounds		
Ending sounds		
Writing letters and words		
Recognizing initial / final consonants		
Recognizing short vowel sounds		
Recognizing long vowel sounds		
Consonant blends		
Consonant digraphs		

Diploma

Awarded to

for extraordinary achievement in K—1 Basic Skills

on this date,

CONGRATULATIONS!

Smart Kid